Solar Applications in Agriculture

Solar Applications in Agriculture

Dr. Robert N. Brewer
Department of Poultry Science
Auburn University
Auburn, Alabama

Dr. Clifford A. Flood, Jr.
Department of Agricultural Engineering
Auburn University
Auburn, Alabama

Dr. Elwynn S. Taylor
Department of Agronomy and Soils
Iowa State University
Ames, Iowa

Dr. Joe L. Koon
Department of Agricultural Engineering
Auburn University
Auburn, Alabama

Dr. Morris White
Department of Agricultural Economics
and Rural Sociology
Auburn University
Auburn, Alabama

Current printing (last digit):
5 4 3 2 1

ISBN: 0-89168-034-9
Library of Congress Catalog Card Number: 81-1154

Printed in the United States of America

TABLE OF CONTENTS

TABLE OF CONTENTS (Continued)

I. INTRODUCTION

Solar energy is directly or indirectly vital to all human activity, but is uniquely important to agriculture. Figure I-1 illustrates some common methods, either geophysical (natural) or mechanical (engineered collection), of harnessing solar energy for agricultural use. The most basic means of natural exploitation is photosynthesis, the process in plants by which the sun's rays convert water and carbon dioxide into the life-sustaining chemical form of sugar.

Photosynthesis underlies all food and fiber production. Field, garden, and forest crops collect energy directly from the sun and store it in the course of their growth. These products are then consumed as human or animal food, manufactured into hundreds of secondary materials or devices necessary to provide shelter and enhance the quality of life, burned as a primary source of heat, or chemically converted into liquid or gaseous fuels.

Fossil fuels such as petroleum, natural gas, and coal, on which our present energy systems largely depend, owe their existence to photosynthesis in earlier geologic eras. Formed slowly over millions of years, these resources are finite and rapidly decreasing. To spare this depletable fossil stock, full advantage must be taken of the possibilities for converting solar energy into useful forms.

Thermal energy direct from the sun also creates atmospheric temperature and pressure differences which generate air currents. Windmills and turbines can transform these currents into mechanical work such as pumping water for livestock and domestic use and for filling surface ponds to supply irrigation channels. Ocean thermal energy conversion (OTEC) systems can also drive heat engines with the temperature difference between sun-warmed upper layers and cooler deep layers in the ocean. However, technical progress in this area has not kept pace with advances in other forms of solar energy conversion, and such offshore energy sources are inconvenient for agricultural applications.

Perhaps the most important agricultural benefits of direct solar energy are the drying of soils to a suitable condition for planting crops and the maturation and drying of crops in the field to permit timely and efficient harvesting. As food and fiber crops mature, their moisture content is typically allowed to decrease to 20-35% before harvest. After harvest, crops must be mechanically dried further to a 10-13% moisture content for safe storage with minimal deterioration.[1] The mechanical drying process may involve the collection, storage, and controlled use of solar energy.

1

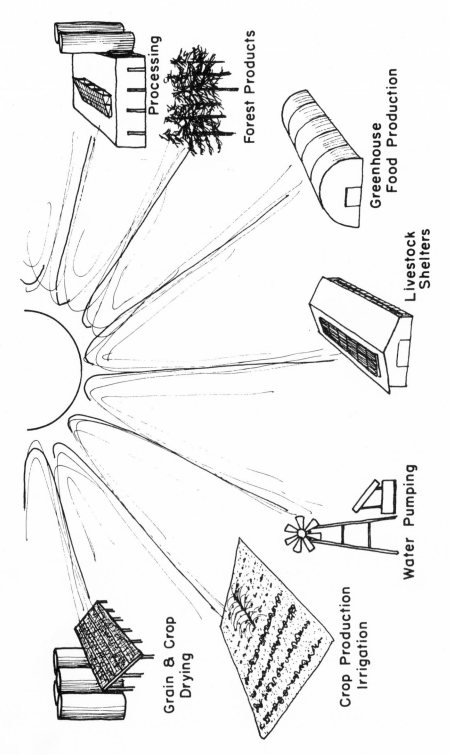

Figure I-1. *Agricultural uses of solar energy*

Agricultural Energy Usage

Science and technology have stimulated an agricultural revolution in the United States during the past century which has produced an abundant supply of safe, wholesome, high quality food.[2] Elements of the revolution included mechanization, the wise use of fertile lands supplemented with chemical fertilizers, pest control, improved management, and sources of unlimited and inexpensive energy.

Development of the internal combustion engine allowed man to replace animal with mechanical power. As tractors and other farm machines became more capable and efficient, agricultural output expanded rapidly until one U.S. farmer can now produce enough food for himself and 50 others. However, much of this capability depends on the assurance of a readily available and economical energy supply.

How much energy does agriculture need? In spite of large-scale production, agriculture by itself consumes only 2.4% of all the energy used in the United States. If we include energy required by the entire food supply system from farm to dinner table, the proportion rises to 13.5% of the total, divided in 1975 as shown in Figure I-2.[3]

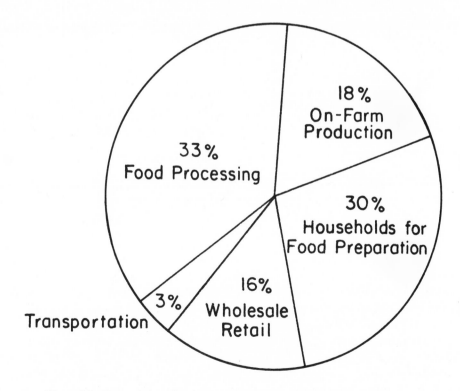

Figure I-2. *Energy usage for food system — from production to table*

Although this was true in 1975, energy requirements are not static. At present, worldwide cultivation averages less than one acre of arable land per person and the ratio is shrinking as population increases. As the world population grows from 4 billion in 1978 to a projected 6 billion in the year 2000 (see Figure I-3[4,5]), food production must become even more intensive. How will agriculture fill the increased demand for energy to ensure adequate food supplies?

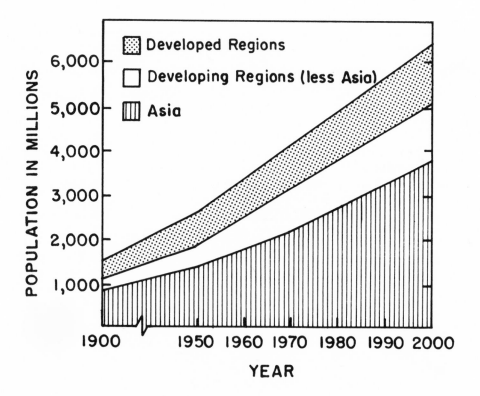

Figure I-3. *World population projected to year 2000*

Many ways are available, but they will require massive capital expenditures, worldwide political cooperation, and a consideration of social and environmental consequences as well as direct economic costs and benefits. New reserves of oil and gas are being discovered and developed each year. Discoveries in Mexico and other areas of the Western Hemisphere have made world-availability charts of only two years ago obsolete! Coal, which may constitute as much as 90% of our fossil fuel reserves, must be exploited, but in a manner compatible with environmental standards. Nuclear technology holds hope for filling part of our future energy needs, but cost and environmental hazards are of major concern to many people. Hydroelectric power and power generation by burning fossil fuels will remain, but must become more efficient.

These energy sources are needed to supply not only power but also the raw materials for fertilizers, pesticides, and other products used in food production. Dr. Norman Borlaug, recipient of the 1970 Nobel Peace Prize for his distinguished contribution to the Green Revolution, has stated, ". . . if agriculture is denied the use of chemical fertilizers and pesticides, the world will be doomed, not by chemical poisoning but by starvation."

This monograph examines the role that solar energy is now playing and can reasonably be expected to play in the future in the production of food and fiber. The diffuse distribution of incoming solar energy makes it best suited for relatively low-temperature agricultural applications requiring less than about 38°C (100°F). Among the most promising areas are:

> General low-temperature heating
> Grain and crop drying
> Heating livestock structures
> Heating greenhouses
> Agricultural processing
> Crop irrigation

Although the temperature levels for these applications are within the appropriate range, the demand is usually for large quantities of heat so that system design must ensure efficient and adequate energy collection, storage, and delivery to the point of need. Not only must the technology be well planned, but a careful assessment must be made of the uncertainties in the local availability of solar radiation due to varying weather.

INTRODUCTION

References

1. D.B. Brooker, F.W. Bakker-Arkema, and C.W. Hall, *Drying Cereal Grains,* AVI Publishing Co., Westport, Connecticut, 1974.
2. R.M. Kottman, "Future Prospects for World Food Production," *Proceedings Conference on Solar Energy for Heating Greenhouses and Greenhouse-Residence Combinations,* U.S. Dept. of Energy, Cleveland, Ohio, March 1977.
3. R.H. Brown, "Energy in Agriculture and Food," *Proceedings Conference on Energy in Agriculture,* Atlanta, Georgia, October 1975.
4. W.J. Chancellor et al, *A Hungry World, Challenge to Agriculture,* University of California Food Task Force, Davis, California, 1974.
5. W.J. Chancellor and J.R. Goss, *Balancing Energy and Food Production 1975-2000,* presented at the 68th Annual Meeting, American Society of Agricultural Engineers, Davis, California, June 1975.

II. CLIMATE

The comfort and well-being of humans and livestock, the health of growing plants, and such agricultural operations as drying and storing of grain ultimately depend on the physical environment. Climate influences both the demand for and supply of energy, that is, the requirements for supplemental energy to counteract adverse climatic conditions and the availability of such energy from the sun.

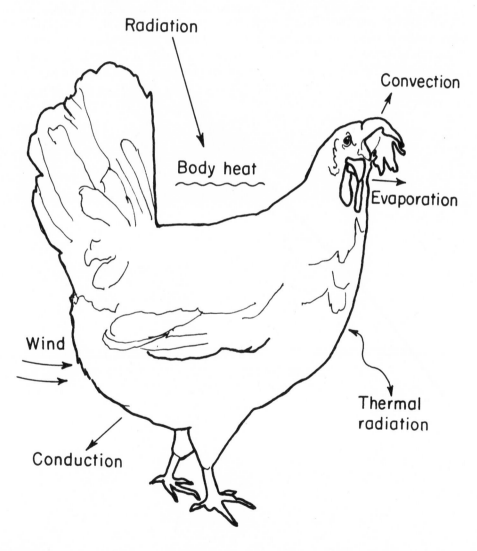

Figure II-1. *Heat gains and losses that must be balanced to control environment of confined livestock*

Environmental Heat Exchange

Warm-blooded animals produce enough body heat to keep sufficiently warm under most natural circumstances where they can find shelter as required. However, when livestock is confined in areas convenient to man, attention must be given to the maintenance of environmental conditions that enable biological temperature-regulating systems to keep body temperatures within acceptable limits. The animals' comfort depends on a balance between heat losses and gains (Figure II-1).

Heat is lost to the surroundings by thermal radiation (all bodies radiate heat at a rate that depends on body temperature and the nature of the radiating surface); by evaporation of water from the skin and exhalation of warm, moist air from the lungs; by convection of heat by moving, cooler air; and by conduction to cooler objects with which the body comes in contact. Evaporation and convection losses depend on the air's temperature, humidity, and speed. Heat is gained from body metabolism, contact with air or objects warmer than the body, thermal radiation from the surroundings, and rays from the sun.

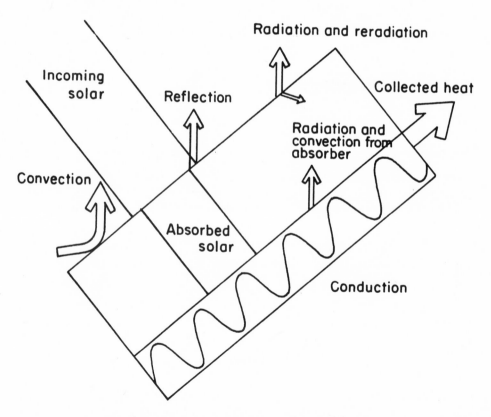

Figure II-2. *Energy exchange at a solar radiation collector*

The same environmental factors affect the heating, cooling, and drying of agricultural crops, whether it is the drying of a single kernel of corn or the cooling of a grain-filled bin. Unlike the case of animals, body heat in stored grains is usually negligible, but fermentation must sometimes be taken into account.

Building heating and cooling also depend on climatic variables as well as on the quality of building design. Unfortunately, generations of accumulated wisdom in designing heat-efficient structures seemed to have been forgotten by schools and practicing architects from the 1940s to the early 1970s. For example, insulation in new buildings was often inadequate. Full glass walls, although esthetically pleasing, admitted sunlight into areas where it was unneeded or even undesirable. The attitude was that the internal environment could always be corrected with the heating and air-conditioning systems.

A reawakening to weather considerations in shelter design will be painful for many, for example, the homeowner whose garage blocks the welcome morning sun from living areas, but whose wall exposure allows overheating by the afternoon sun. These and similar architectural defects, whether in homes, livestock facilities, or business buildings, may remain for the life of the structures because they are not easy or economical to correct.

Careful design of new structures can promote greater comfort, utility, and economy. Building orientation with proper regard for prevailing winds and solar heat load; windows, walls, and shaded areas suitably placed or exposed to derive seasonal benefits; and general common sense in building location and design features can all contribute to lessening the energy requirements.

Climatic variables also influence the performance of solar-heat collectors themselves as well as the energy requirements they serve. The variables are principally wind, temperature, humidity, precipitation, thermal radiation from the surroundings, and, especially, radiation from the sun (Figure II-2).

Effect of Climate on Solar Heating

Wind

Much has been written about the effect of wind on building heating requirements but very little about its influence on the operating efficiency of solar collectors.

Since the outer surfaces of even well insulated collectors become warmer than the surrounding air, they lose heat to the air. How much heat is lost this way depends on the collector's operating temperature, the effectiveness of insulation between the absorbing surface and the cover, and the air temperature and speed. Although other factors also decrease collector efficiency, the contribution of wind is significant.

Collector efficiency reports are usually based on incident solar radiation, air and collector temperatures, and useful delivered heat. Unfortunately, although wind speed may also be reported, convective losses cannot easily be calculated by the average reader of an efficiency report. Some precautions are advisable to compensate for the lack of the necessarily complex heat-loss analysis.

Convective losses are a linear function of wind speed. A collector with a given reported efficiency based on tests in still air is likely to be inferior to one with the same reported efficiency based on tests in a wind of measurable speed. This should be taken into account if a selected collector is to be installed in a windier location than the one in which its efficiency was tested. Structural stability in wind is usually tested, but not efficiency.

Temperature

Air temperature largely determines the need to heat or cool structures and directly influences the output of solar collectors. Collectors that operate at temperatures substantially above that of their surroundings lose more heat, with a resulting decrease in efficiency, than do lower temperature collectors. Efficiency ratings are usually linked to specific temperature differences between the collector plate and the environmental air. If operated in areas where the temperature difference is likely to be greater, the collector's effective efficiency may be much lower than that determined by bench tests.

Just as collector heat losses vary with differences between internal and external temperatures, so do building heat losses. Insulation is desirable not because it changes the basic relationship, but because it slows the rate of heat flow and thereby conserves energy in a heated structure during any given time interval.

Humidity

An appropriate level of atmospheric moisture within a structure is important to the health and well-being of occupants; in the case of poultry, it can be critical. Moisture is also a dominant factor in grain drying and storage. If ventilation is essential for temperature and/or moisture control, environmental humidity is a primary consideration in the determination of the required air flow and heating. It therefore directly affects the demand placed upon a solar heating system.

Precipitation

Rain does not seriously affect solar collectors, although it does imply the absence of sunshine. However, snow and hail can be harmful. Snow coats the surface of tilted, exposed collectors and can greatly limit their utility in cold climates. Hail is a minor threat to vertical glass but a major hazard to tilted glass surfaces in areas where hail is common. Collector selection should take into account regional snow and hail conditions.

Thermal Radiation

All bodies radiate heat at a rate that rises with their temperature and absorb heat from the radiating bodies around them. The rate of heat emission at a given temperature varies according to the surface property called *emissivity*, the maximum possible rate being that from a perfect "black body" with an emissivity of 1. Emissivity also expresses the fraction of incoming radiation that is absorbed (the rest is transmitted or reflected). A warm body surrounded by cold bodies tends to emit more heat than it absorbs, and a cold body surrounded by warm bodies tends to absorb more than it emits. When emission and absorption are equal, the body is in thermal equilibrium with respect to radiation.

These effects are felt by humans and livestock and explain why a high air temperature alone often fails to give a sense of warm comfort. For example, a higher room temperature is necessary in winter than in summer to make occupants feel comfortable. This is because colder ceilings and walls in winter create an imbalance in radiation exchange that is felt in spite of a reassuring thermometer reading. Since radiation passes through transparent glass, the cold outdoors also has an effect in a room with windows.

Sheltered livestock can tolerate a wide range of air temperatures (a reduced load on a solar heating system) if their environment provides a favorable level of thermal radiation. Also, low emissivity coatings developed for solar collectors reduce the heat lost by radiation (surfaces designed to absorb solar radiation must have high emissivity).

Sunshine

The sun is the ultimate source of our energy. Solar radiation strikes the outer atmosphere at a nearly constant rate of 439 Btu per square foot per hour. (The literature contains various energy units, such as the kilowatt-hour and the traditional, but obsolete, Langley; eventually all, including the Btu, will be replaced by units of the International System in which energy is expressed in joules, area in square meters, and time in seconds. 439 Btu = 1.384 kilojoules per square meter per second.) This radiation is considerably reduced by atmospheric absorption, scattering, and reflection before reaching the earth's surface. The insolation (solar radiation incident on the surface) can be calculated from estimates of atmospheric turbidity, but is preferably measured for greater accuracy.

Insolation Measurements

Several instruments measure either total incident radiant energy or illumination (the visible portion of the spectrum). Illumination meters are usually less expensive than radiation instruments and easier for the layman to obtain and operate. However, their readings of partial radiation are not easy to convert into accurate total radiation figures. Approximate values for total solar radiation in Btu per square foot per hour can be calculated by multiplying illumination readings in foot candles by 0.033 if the sky is clear, and by 0.031 if it is cloudy.

The most common instrument for measuring insolation is the global pyranometer. This instrument responds not only to the broad solar spectrum, but also to both direct (in line with the sun) and diffuse (from all angles above the horizon) radiation that falls on a horizontal surface (Figure II-3)[1]. The pyranometer can be fitted with colored filters to measure energy only in selected spectral bands, or shielded to block direct solar rays from the sensor so that only diffuse radiation is measured (shadow band). Subtracting the shielded from the unshielded measurement gives the direct component of the insolation on the horizontal surface.

Another radiation instrument is the pyrheliometer which measures only the direct solar radiation incident on a surface at right angles to the direct beam. The pyrheliometer is generally used to track the path of the sun.

Measurements of solar radiation in the past have been sporadic compared with other meteorological measurements such as precipitation and temperature. Also, their accuracy has often been questionable. The records have been subjected to much professional scrutiny, and solar climatology data for the United States, considered reliable enough for planning and design purposes, are available from the National Climate Center, Asheville, N.C.

Geographic Distribution of Insolation

Existing insolation records provide a basis for calculating the average energy received at given locations. Solar climate maps (Figure II-4)[2] are readily available and show insolation contours. The user can interpolate between contours to estimate values at sites where measurements have not been made. However, the maps are not precise, and abnormal atmospheric conditions can cause large deviations from average insolation values from year to year.

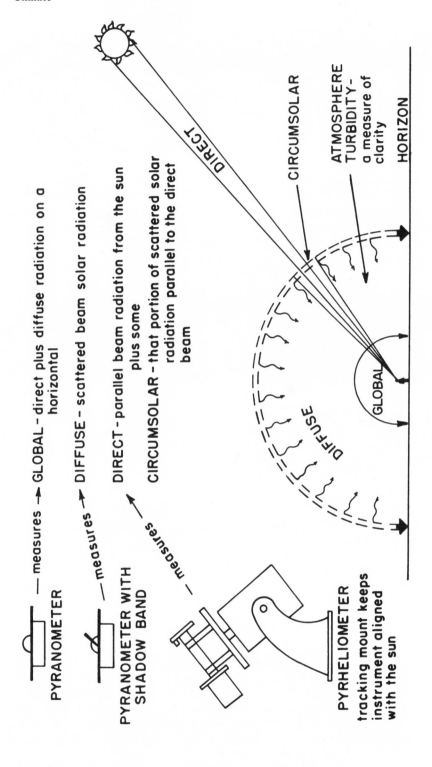

— measures → GLOBAL - direct plus diffuse radiation on a horizontal

PYRANOMETER

— measures → DIFFUSE - scattered beam solar radiation

PYRANOMETER WITH SHADOW BAND

— measures → DIRECT - parallel beam radiation from the sun plus some

CIRCUMSOLAR - that portion of scattered solar radiation parallel to the direct beam

PYRHELIOMETER tracking mount keeps instrument aligned with the sun

CIRCUMSOLAR

ATMOSPHERE TURBIDITY- a measure of clarity

HORIZON

DIRECT

GLOBAL

DIFFUSE

Figure II-3. *Insolation types and meters* (from *Guide to Solar Energy Programs*, U.S. Department of Energy, 061-00-00042-9, June 1978)

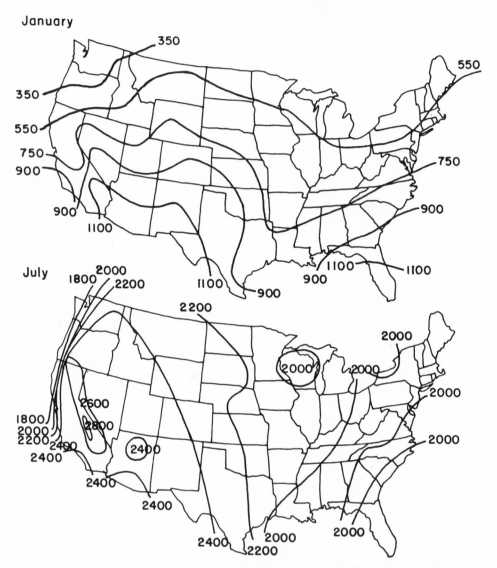

Figure II-4. *Mean daily insolation in Btu/ft² for January and July* (from *Minimum Property Standards for Solar Heating,* Vol. 5, Dept. of Housing & Urban Development, Washington, D.C., 1977)

The probability of receiving a given amount of radiation during a particular time interval is more useful than an average annual value for engineering planning and design. Tables II-1 through II-3 are representative solar probability tables based by Getz and Nicholas[3] on accumulated U.S. National Weather Service data. They show, for example, that during the week of December 6–12, the records indicate a 90% chance that the daily solar radiation falling on each square meter of surface will

Table II-1. Solar radiation in kJ/m² per day by climatic week at Boston, Mass., July 1952–November 1968 (adapted from Getz and Nicholas[3])

CLIMATIC WEEK	NUMBER OBS	MINIMUM RADIATION	MAXIMUM RADIATION	MEAN RADIATION	STD OF MEAN	PROBABILITY IN PERCENT OF RECEIVING AT LEAST THE INDICATED AMOUNT								
						95	90	80	70	50 (MEDIAN)	30	20	10	5
03/01 – 03/07	112	840	16905	9229	485	2109	3431	4431	7317	9797	12179	13727	14502	15350
03/08 – 03/14	112	632	18521	10500	519	2254	4167	6237	9682	11271	13012	15013	16103	16679
03/15 – 03/21	112	1135	20497	11950	567	2938	5008	6938	10162	13096	15700	16968	18011	18725
03/22 – 03/28	112	650	20914	13682	592	3575	5982	7243	10042	13616	16175	17670	18417	19847
03/29 – 04/04	112	1173	23305	13743	670	3363	4939	6652	10711	12772	15397	18010	19674	21503
04/05 – 04/11	112	893	24310	14493	686	3627	5677	7243	10711	14888	18059	20937	21930	22632
04/12 – 04/18	112	1251	24610	15287	687	3430	5677	7304	11231	14430	17083	20867	22406	23496
04/19 – 04/25	112	928	25593	15606	746	3887	5561	7887	11977	14731	18059	22389	23115	24645
04/26 – 05/02	112	1204	28644	16091	842	3239	4846	7887	9076	16091	19076	23680	25020	25707
05/03 – 05/09	112	1361	29306	17599	792	4760	5677	9561	13534	17586	20451	24651	26203	26944
05/10 – 05/16	112	1655	29306	18288	779	4781	7360	9080	14731	18288	21367	24651	25813	27450
05/17 – 05/23	112	2003	30960	19454	685	7697	11892	13959	17360	19843	22466	24915	25471	27313
05/24 – 05/30	112	1992	31400	20268	733	7168	11189	13506	16789	21110	23520	25896	27471	28463
05/31 – 06/06	112	2915	30727	20867	748	7181	11968	13848	17438	20891	23219	25388	27004	28846
06/07 – 06/13	112	2190	32993	19286	810	5911	9670	13848	17438	19286	23520	26196	27233	28630
06/14 – 06/20	112	1631	30945	21408	788	5722	13506	16489	19594	21985	24064	25983	28334	29194
06/21 – 06/27	112	3979	31324	20521	736	7113	12223	16055	18102	21850	23535	24813	26390	27771
06/28 – 07/04	119	3635	31069	22055	607	10577	16489	17625	21678	23732	25030	25716	26922	27943
07/05 – 07/11	119	3547	30520	20658	610	10334	16055	18102	21850	23535	25152	26390	26626	27886
07/12 – 07/18	119	1927	28984	19217	662	8035	10899	15104	18402	20969	23260	24388	25603	26943
07/19 – 07/25	119	2498	33270	18642	603	8001	10334	15945	18013	20969	23260	24552	24671	26380
07/26 – 08/01	119	2878	30392	19678	569	10402	12175	14153	19999	20649	22769	23764	24552	25936
08/02 – 08/08	119	2490	26093	17705	581	7548	11768	13813	17597	19337	21332	22662	23252	24241
08/09 – 08/15	119	2340	25820	16520	585	5734	10670	13896	14367	17924	19515	20932	21984	23629
08/16 – 08/22	119	290	24850	16999	556	6603	12082	14699	16710	18753	20073	20987	21816	23510
08/23 – 08/29	119	2157	24804	16413	577	4836	10334	14153	16220	18337	19502	20739	21875	22954
08/30 – 09/05	119	1198	23540	15755	529	6849	9662	12728	15459	16972	19247	20345	20974	21856
09/06 – 09/12	119	786	22667	15692	540	5874	9690	13285	16248	17855	19125	20296	20731	21593
09/13 – 09/19	119	1037	22264	13812	545	3946	7466	11045	13238	15780	17063	18055	19329	20153
09/20 – 09/26	119	659	19802	13236	487	4392	6843	10913	13431	15000	15983	18000	18000	18710
09/27 – 10/03	119	640	19470	12305	491	2332	6176	10849	12424	13398	15867	14247	16943	17386
10/04 – 10/10	119	614	17546	10990	488	2435	4492	7693	11360	12854	14247	15383	16064	16363
10/11 – 10/17	119	373	17672	11157	382	4028	7305	7403	9056	10383	13359	13948	14544	15006
10/18 – 10/24	119	691	16354	9158	398	1884	3485	2038	7504	12577	11602	12367	12879	13658
10/25 – 10/31	119	730	13416	7927	357	1688	3328	2848	4796	9473	10292	10700	11685	12238
11/01 – 11/07	119	287	12078	6525	334	1097	2109	2109	3578	8245	9473	9327	10204	10796
11/08 – 11/14	119	477	10427	6024	283	1392	2666	3578	5043	6999	7736	8363	9242	9658
11/15 – 11/21	119	174	10101	5526	264	1581	2299	3079	4481	6361	5680	8027	8429	9106
11/22 – 11/28	112	219	8829	4974	246	1116	1992	2643	3980	5678	6452	7229	7739	8031
11/29 – 12/05	112	475	8191	5076	233	979	2113	3401	4958	6003	6365	7001	7457	7687
12/06 – 12/12	112	100	7557	4076	218	940	2035	2848	4404	4360	5208	5753	6460	7030
12/13 – 12/19	112	200	7613	4582	208	1240	2038	3401	4404	5139	5926	6296	6737	7103
12/20 – 12/26	112	197	7720	4613	216	1086	2848	2848	4268	5369	5891	6334	6765	7035
12/27 – 01/02	112	142	7598	4771	214	1456	1884	2994	4375	5459	6081	6610	6984	7207
01/03 – 01/09	112	149	7928	4771	228	1198	1797	3306	4133	5203	6223	6660	7164	7504
01/10 – 01/16	112	95	9343	5133	279	1018	1829	2230	4155	6309	7301	7508	7508	8187
01/17 – 01/23	112	211	9273	5764	250	1829	2622	3763	5223	6309	6526	7548	7986	8490
01/24 – 01/30	112	159	10152	5812	299	1733	2323	3204	5106	6526	6406	7887	8250	9446
01/31 – 02/06	112	866	11273	6792	294	1274	3591	3204	5864	7501	7435	8525	8989	9446
02/07 – 02/13	112	567	13736	7344	350	2226	2986	4528	6287	7858	8490	9422	9885	10329
02/14 – 02/20	112	353	14337	8622	392	1534	3460	4644	6803	9364	10154	10546	10984	11561
02/21 – 02/27	112	944	15408	9357	417	1831	4159	7490	9322	11948	10499	12740	12125	13724

Table II-2. Solar radiation in kJ/m² per day by climatic week at Columbia, Mo., July 1952–December 1975 (adapted from Getz and Nicholas[3])

CLIMATIC WEEK	NUMBER OBS	MINIMUM RADIATION	MAXIMUM RADIATION	MEAN RADIATION	STD OF MEAN	PROBABILITY IN PERCENT OF RECEIVING AT LEAST THE INDICATED AMOUNT								
						90	80	70	60	50 (MEDIAN)	40	30	20	10
03/01 - 03/07	161	712	20675	12337	453	2987	5664	8840	11806	14706	15655	16768	17622	18375
03/08 - 03/14	161	62	20618	12331	470	3786	6130	9392	12694	12938	14755	15114	17074	18640
03/15 - 03/21	161	584	23222	13621	538	2834	5614	9392	12694	14755	15117	19117	20137	21172
03/22 - 03/28	161	456	23803	14462	542	4121	7761	9507	12511	16327	18437	20230	21238	22156
03/29 - 04/04	161	1147	24658	14608	569	4428	7086	9101	11501	15632	18644	20536	22023	23161
04/05 - 04/11	161	1219	26013	17743	584	5320	9846	11854	15289	18936	21860	23095	24522	24954
04/12 - 04/18	161	1831	27203	17201	586	5869	9763	14432	16452	19107	22846	24680	24522	25537
04/19 - 04/25	161	1749	29528	18433	600	6342	9618	14632	17627	20604	22994	24560	26008	26717
04/26 - 05/02	161	2439	29198	18995	597	7279	11390	17816	20486	22685	24543	26635	26741	27915
05/03 - 05/09	161	3305	30460	20663	600	8139	13343	16797	20386	23370	25432	27012	27686	28419
05/10 - 05/16	161	3237	31349	20869	621	7734	12845	16775	20208	24583	26327	27872	28134	29259
05/17 - 05/23	161	1372	30554	22034	595	9701	14942	19525	22208	23878	26024	27923	28519	29640
05/24 - 05/30	161	4063	32000	21618	591	10427	13975	16775	20224	25413	26852	27408	28860	29841
05/31 - 06/06	161	3150	32123	22068	585	10781	14829	18081	21925	24624	27542	27941	28889	30033
06/07 - 06/13	161	4243	31702	23187	539	12708	16402	20856	22728	25070	28527	29153	29083	30380
06/14 - 06/20	161	2728	31934	23939	515	14496	19260	21322	23546	25468	27542	29150	29182	30577
06/21 - 06/27	161	6014	33544	24616	515	13080	18998	22047	25073	27114	28424	29153	29868	30724
06/28 - 07/04	168	5114	32064	24977	440	16611	19654	23992	24982	26511	27900	29067	29658	30239
07/05 - 07/11	168	6691	32475	25154	441	16151	20134	22018	25527	26876	28121	29818	29818	30315
07/12 - 07/18	168	6397	32339	23762	478	12742	18132	18132	24345	25825	27076	29067	28750	29584
07/19 - 07/25	168	3167	30128	23127	462	14491	18169	21054	23741	25296	26479	27449	28001	28663
07/26 - 08/01	168	3840	30425	23133	457	13973	18646	21349	23753	25214	26080	27335	27916	28421
08/02 - 08/08	168	4674	28827	22047	483	11863	17272	19865	23160	24425	25562	26277	27098	27625
08/09 - 08/15	168	3730	29298	21715	457	11937	16961	16961	22646	23515	24765	25373	26636	26942
08/16 - 08/22	168	4682	28068	20986	419	11699	17656	20789	22964	23515	23631	24364	25226	25896
08/23 - 08/29	168	2706	27316	21114	375	14219	18531	19841	21684	21644	23374	24017	24668	25249
08/30 - 09/05	168	2368	25125	18565	438	10125	13933	18531	21644	20897	21868	22787	23423	23817
09/06 - 09/12	168	4023	24090	18520	393	10242	14626	16034	18992	20224	21159	22106	22636	22969
09/13 - 09/19	168	825	22665	15601	464	6154	9032	13047	18030	17843	18797	20037	21147	21713
09/20 - 09/26	168	1494	21559	14503	437	5456	8454	11444	13491	16201	17729	19142	19900	20471
09/27 - 10/03	168	2034	20782	15716	369	7708	11035	12231	14925	16431	17957	19067	19375	19772
10/04 - 10/10	168	477	19273	13757	421	3709	7147	11713	12926	16277	17336	19067	18096	18406
10/11 - 10/17	168	367	17622	12630	347	4735	8424	10783	14211	14925	15309	17713	16486	16897
10/18 - 10/24	168	1519	17298	12002	350	3602	6885	10291	12473	14211	14808	15859	15694	16131
10/25 - 10/31	168	1069	15566	10208	355	2956	4717	7276	9992	12028	13249	15344	14470	14794
11/01 - 11/07	168	968	14641	8836	320	2696	4083	5738	7773	9945	11341	12177	12998	13685
11/08 - 11/14	168	414	14043	8463	308	2128	3610	6146	7606	9899	10954	11934	12232	12566
11/15 - 11/21	168	408	12457	7454	291	1955	3203	5104	6389	8969	9715	10651	12217	11530
11/22 - 11/28	168	274	11280	7306	250	2256	2901	4116	5859	8242	9096	10070	10437	10798
11/29 - 12/05	168	276	11323	6673	252	1743	2778	4287	5104	7548	8739	9431	9943	10265
12/06 - 12/12	168	313	11499	5874	261	1273	1788	3110	4558	6107	7903	8746	9518	9811
12/13 - 12/19	168	253	11233	6071	232	1701	2132	3551	4411	6545	7612	8476	9266	9627
12/20 - 12/26	168	424	10844	5717	249	1396	2325	2925	5045	5572	7382	8327	8966	9983
12/27 - 01/02	168	639	10670	5992	250	1764	3077	3433	4658	6149	7336	8562	9539	10050
01/03 - 01/09	161	479	11157	6751	250	1580	3045	4923	6796	7853	8617	9264	9602	9989
01/10 - 01/16	161	1035	12805	6712	254	1771	2379	4280	6110	7197	8539	9230	9777	9777
01/17 - 01/23	161	623	12670	6654	289	1380	3193	3983	5405	7083	8298	9376	10385	10397
01/24 - 01/30	161	552	13581	7696	316	1993	2973	4134	6165	9013	10288	11056	11056	11174
01/31 - 02/06	161	666	15634	8227	343	2214	4117	4729	7030	8993	10527	11841	11649	12094
02/07 - 02/13	161	618	15603	9324	359	2470	6310	7763	9689	9957	12177	13259	13852	14587
02/14 - 02/20	161	645	17010	10599	368	3183	5566	7569	9689	11973	13137	14313	15017	15746
02/21 - 02/27	161	832	20978	10659	462	2475	3524	5248	9176	11664	14439	15680	16511	17015

Table II-3. Solar radiation in kJ/m² per day by climatic week at El Paso, Tx., July 1952–December 1975 (adapted from Getz and Nicholas[3])

CLIMATIC WEEK	NUMBER OBS	MINIMUM RADIATION	MAXIMUM RADIATION	MEAN RADIATION	STD OF MEAN	\(\text{PROBABILITY IN PERCENT OF RECEIVING AT LEAST THE INDICATED AMOUNT}\)								
						90	80	70	60	50 (MEDIAN)	40	30	20	10
03/01 - 03/07	161	7570	23340	19480	297	12907	16630	19010	20214	21322	21635	21909	22157	22516
03/08 - 03/14	161	6722	24606	20731	322	13525	18668	20693	21725	22180	22880	23194	23545	23766
03/15 - 03/21	161	4978	26497	21643	359	15385	19176	21176	22479	23691	24103	24469	24752	25065
03/22 - 03/28	161	10838	27668	23718	768	18987	21433	23020	23982	25053	25504	25910	26198	26472
03/29 - 04/04	161	9815	28303	24629	288	18495	21623	24347	25563	26179	26600	26903	27243	27627
04/05 - 04/11	161	9913	29457	26101	264	21037	23866	26029	26926	27347	27676	27972	28277	28680
04/12 - 04/18	161	9880	30825	26774	324	19907	25045	26974	27825	28309	28555	29133	29334	29734
04/19 - 04/25	161	6684	31992	27851	319	23576	26500	28048	28686	29298	29555	29921	29934	30188
04/26 - 05/02	161	7322	32244	27923	377	20032	26091	28176	29247	29893	30299	30595	30810	31170
05/03 - 05/09	161	12880	33031	29104	276	24167	26951	29584	30433	30823	31102	31428	31672	31838
05/10 - 05/16	161	4652	33496	29375	347	24566	27329	29604	30621	31058	31395	31676	32000	32406
05/17 - 05/23	161	13348	33976	30103	249	25877	28574	30117	30823	31373	31686	31846	32225	32702
05/24 - 05/30	161	11621	34040	29951	286	25058	28397	30019	30962	31580	31948	32102	32481	32971
05/31 - 06/06	161	9678	34013	30077	320	25049	28394	30031	30831	31697	32031	32141	32631	33227
06/07 - 06/13	161	10579	34295	30344	302	24609	28374	30262	30787	31948	32374	32678	33003	33395
06/14 - 06/20	161	17002	34704	31103	222	28047	30252	31476	31580	32116	32678	32877	33003	33234
06/21 - 06/27	168	8600	34090	30495	287	24416	27951	30297	30869	31632	31969	32426	32877	32779
06/28 - 07/04	168	7300	33955	29482	351	19189	24392	27265	30055	31341	31640	31187	32080	32770
07/05 - 07/11	168	9399	33753	27956	404	23495	25982	27508	29752	30716	31187	31640	31901	32296
07/12 - 07/18	168	10598	33125	28254	318	21166	24997	26621	28411	30117	30479	30927	31332	31736
07/19 - 07/25	168	11505	32958	27661	324	20330	22775	24514	27427	29752	30159	30567	30974	31381
07/26 - 08/01	168	11187	32361	26358	321	21901	24447	25524	27589	29161	29508	29855	30202	30548
08/02 - 08/08	168	6710	31211	26906	296	21647	23422	25257	27093	28925	29250	29576	29901	30226
08/09 - 08/15	168	15041	31232	26659	268	21150	23146	24399	26468	28130	28594	29058	29522	29986
08/16 - 08/22	168	10828	30543	25493	277	18385	22468	23989	26249	28139	28435	28730	29026	29321
08/23 - 08/29	168	7149	30034	25043	312	18528	22648	23037	25694	27217	27611	28005	28399	28793
08/30 - 09/05	168	3980	28746	24132	346	17737	21463	22521	24865	26567	26977	27386	27795	28205
09/06 - 09/12	168	8870	27440	23338	297	17028	21098	21715	24258	25837	26220	26602	26985	27367
09/13 - 09/19	168	6037	25974	22560	283	13829	20867	21124	23515	24838	25205	25572	25938	26305
09/20 - 09/26	168	3500	25090	20697	352	15052	18670	20482	22017	23690	24064	24438	24811	25185
09/27 - 10/03	168	3689	24500	21367	336	15815	18875	20405	21936	23466	23717	23967	24217	24467
10/04 - 10/10	168	4704	23558	20193	262	15510	17933	19507	21081	22656	22848	23040	23231	23423
10/11 - 10/17	168	2709	22473	19288	246	12924	17011	18532	20053	21574	21759	21944	22129	22314
10/18 - 10/24	168	3450	20859	17883	268	11026	14687	16630	18573	20517	20724	20930	21137	21343
10/25 - 10/31	168	2352	19759	16451	277	12017	14884	16336	17789	19241	19445	19648	19852	20055
11/01 - 11/07	168	2513	18556	15797	237	11051	13400	14939	16479	18018	18245	18472	18699	18926
11/08 - 11/14	168	1310	17251	14753	233	10479	12148	13759	15370	16982	17189	17395	17602	17808
11/15 - 11/21	168	4084	16600	13935	193	8080	10030	12023	14016	16009	16175	16340	16506	16671
11/22 - 11/28	168	1530	15466	12583	265	6183	10073	11741	13410	15078	15273	15468	15662	15857
11/29 - 12/05	168	2917	15371	12203	204	7673	10445	11692	12939	14186	14380	14574	14768	14962
12/06 - 12/12	168	1613	14536	11822	223	6365	9029	10468	11908	13347	13560	13772	13985	14197
12/13 - 12/19	168	1176	14051	11295	212	8162	10363	11248	12132	13017	13212	13406	13601	13795
12/20 - 12/26	168	2434	14090	11651	234	5651	8707	10103	11499	12895	13035	13176	13316	13456
12/27 - 01/02	169	1575	14886	11442	257	8612	10991	11697	12404	13110	13216	13322	13428	13533
01/03 - 01/09	168	2138	15045	11493	210	6129	10850	11551	12253	12954	13140	13326	13511	13697
01/10 - 01/16	161	3335	15478	12888	250	7830	13131	13421	13710	14000	14016	14031	14047	14062
01/17 - 01/23	161	2172	16214	12916	247	9146	13460	13780	14100	14420	14486	14552	14618	14684
01/24 - 01/30	161	2043	16919	14066	261	9048	14078	14484	14890	15296	15338	15379	15421	15462
01/31 - 02/06	161	2250	17986	14901	295	9691	14359	14939	15519	16100	16148	16195	16243	16290
02/07 - 02/13	161	2777	18960	15656	295	11295	15103	15784	16465	17147	17226	17305	17384	17462
02/14 - 02/20	161	4342	19319	17370	261	12295	15593	16624	17655	18685	19202	19718	20235	20751
02/21 - 02/27	161	3455	22051	18309	295	12954	16603	17668	18733	19798	20117	20436	20755	21073

total at least 940 kilojoules in Boston, Massachusetts, 1273 kilojoules in Columbia, Missouri, and 7673 kilojoules in El Paso, Texas.

Insolation at a Tilted Collector

Most solar data are for radiation incident on a horizontal surface. If the collector is tilted to face the sun, it receives considerably more energy. To do so continuously would require following the angle of solar incidence which varies with the time of day and day of the year. The sun's path can be calculated from formulas or determined from diagrams like that in Figure II-5.[4]

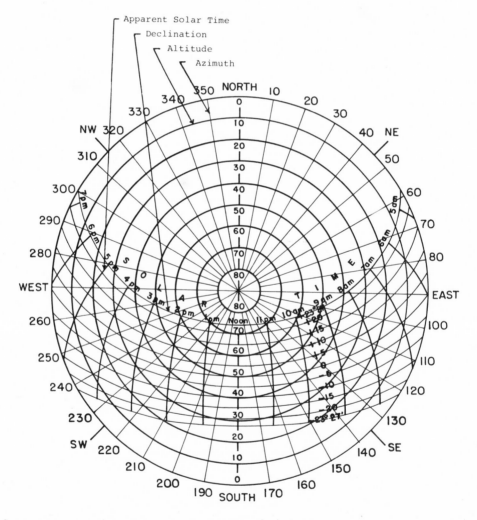

Figure II-5. *Daily and seasonal variation of solar altitude and azimuth for 40°N latitude, true solar time* (from *Smithsonian Meteorological Tables*)

Solar-path diagrams show the sun's varying *altitude* and *azimuth* at the latitude and longitude of the collector site relative to the solar *declination* (season indicator) and time of day expressed in terms of the *apparent*, or *true*, solar time, *AST*. *Altitude* is the angle between the sun-to-earth line and a horizontal plane at the collector site. *Azimuth* is the angle between the north-south line and the projection of the sun-to-earth line on the horizontal plane. *Declination* is the angle between the

Table II-4. Year Date, Declination, and Equation of Time for the 21st day of Each Month

Month	Jan.	Feb.	Mar.	Apr.	May	June	July	Aug.	Sept.	Oct.	Nov.	Dec.
Day of the year	21	52	80	111	141	173	202	233	265	294	325	355
Declination, degrees	−19.9	−10.6	0.0	+11.9	+20.3	+23.45	+20.5	+12.1	0.0	−10.7	−19.9	−23.45
Equation of Time, minutes	−11.2	−13.9	−7.5	+ 1.1	+ 3.3	− 1.4	− 6.2	− 2.4	+7.5	+15.4	+13.8	+ 1.6

sun-to-earth line and a plane through the earth's equator (monthly values are given in Table II-4). The apparent solar time in the United States can be calculated from the equation[5]:

$$AST = Local\ Standard\ Time\ +\ Equation\ of\ Time\ -4m$$

where the *Equation of Time* can be found in Table II-4 for the 21st day of each month, and *m* is the longitude at the collector site in minutes (time not degrees of angle). (The term $4m$ is added, rather than subtracted, for longitudes east of the Greenwich meridian.)

Each latitude for different collector sites requires a different solar-path diagram. The *Smithsonian Meteorological Tables* include diagrams for equatorial to polar latitudes in 5° increments. Figure II-5 is for 40° north. After obtaining the appropriate diagram, the user locates the point with the desired coordinates of *solar time* (scale marked 5 *am* to 7 *pm* on a right-to-left arc near the middle of Figure II-5) and *declination* (scale marked −23.45 to + 23.45 in the lower right quadrant), and then finds the *altitude* and *azimuth* corresponding to the same point. *Altitudes* are concentric circles designated 0–80 on the center vertical scale (the unmarked center of the circles represents 90°, i.e., directly overhead). *Azimuths* are radial lines designated 10–350 where they intersect the outermost circle (*north* represents both 0° and 360°; *south* represents 180°). The *solar time* scale is limited to the hours of potential sunshine.

Since the *declination* remains approximately constant for periods of the order of a few days while the *altitude*, *azimuth*, and *solar time* vary widely during each day, a right-to-left arc representing a particular *declination* also indicates the sun's path as it swings from east to west on a given day. The diagram can thus be used to outline a "solar window" through which a collector positioned at the center of the diagram will be able to "see" the sun as the solar path changes from one *declination* to another with the passage of seasons.

The selection of a collector site should take into account existing or planned trees, structures, terrain features, and other obstacles that might intrude into the solar window to shade part or all of the collector at a time when solar energy is needed. Unless the collector installation will allow a totally unobstructed view of the horizon which is unlikely to become obstructed in the future, drawing of a solar window diagram is advisable.

Figure II-6 illustrates the construction of a solar window for a collector used for winter heating between September 21 and March 21. The basic unobstructed window lies between the *declination* arcs for 0° (September 21 and March 21) and 23.45° (December 21) and between the east and west horizons. The *altitudes* and *azimuths* of the outlines of obstacles are then obtained and the outlines are drawn on the diagram. A magnetic compass can be used to determine the *azimuth*. *Altitudes* can be measured with a protractor, string, and small weight. One end of the string is attached to the weight, which is allowed to hang free, and the other end is attached to the center of the protractor. From the collector position, the user then sights along the straight edge of the protractor, rotating the protractor until the line of sight intersects the top of the obstacle. The vertical string will then pass over the angle marking on the protractor that indicates the *altitude*.

A comparison of Figures II-5 and II-6 shows that this collector will be shaded before 9 AM, at noon, and after 3 PM for a major portion of the September–March period. The severity of the shading problem can be evaluated by reference to a typical daily insolation pattern. Figure II-7 shows such a pattern for a south-facing collector surface tilted upward at an angle approximately equal to the latitude, plus 15° for September and March. Since the sun's position is due south at 12 noon, this time and direction correspond to peak insolation. It is evident that the tree in Figure II-6 located directly south of the collector must be removed if this site is to be used. On the other hand, shading before 8 AM and after 4 PM, when the insolation is very low, will not seriously reduce the total collected energy. Since a solar window diagram shows present shading problems at a particular collector site, and can also be used to predict necessary height restrictions on future structures and plantings to be placed in that vicinity, it is a helpful tool for the prudent farmstead planner.

Flat-plate solar collectors should be oriented to intercept maximum radiation during the season when energy is required. Generally, the collector should face south unless local conditions dictate otherwise. For example, at a site on the western shore of a large body of water, morning haze may reduce incoming radiation. Here, it is good practice to face the collector slightly west of south where it will point directly toward the sun at a later time of day when the air is clearer. On the other hand, if the

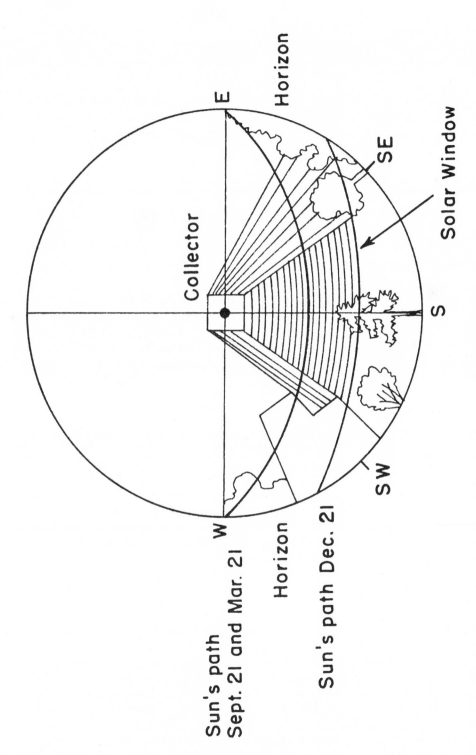

Figure II-6. *Solar window through which a collector can receive radiation from September 21 to March 21, defined by the sun's path at seasonal extremes, with outlines of encroaching obstacles at the collector site*

site has frequent afternoon thundershowers, directing the collector slightly east of south would be more appropriate.

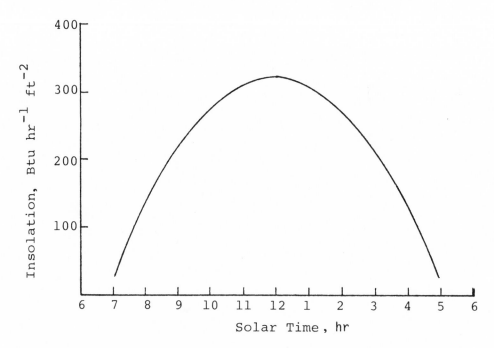

Figure II-7. *Typical daily variation of winter insolation on a south-facing surface*

The collector should also be tilted upward at an angle equal to the site's latitude minus the seasonal declination. Since this would require frequent angle changes, it is not practical. The optimum tilt angle for a fixed installation should equal the latitude if energy needs are constant throughout the year. The angle should be reduced about 15° for summer-only use and increased about 15° for winter-only use (Figure II-8).

Energy Needs and Solar Availability

Solar energy is potentially most useful where it is a suitable form for existing applications, for example, heating water or shelters and drying agricultural products, and where ample solar radiation is available at the collector site. Paradoxically, in some areas such as the southwestern United States, insolation is abundant but little supplemental heat is needed for shelters or grain drying. In other areas with cold, moist climates, heat is needed but the insolation is lacking for economically feasible exploitation. Figure II-9[6] indicates the regions of the United States where need and availability combine to offer the greatest potential for use of solar energy.

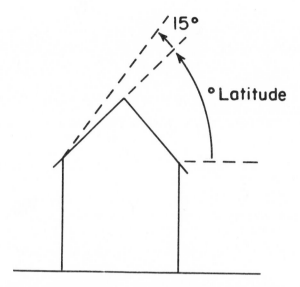

Figure II-8. *Optimum tilt of flat-plate solar collector (equal to angle of latitude at collector site and increased 10-20° for winter-only heating)*

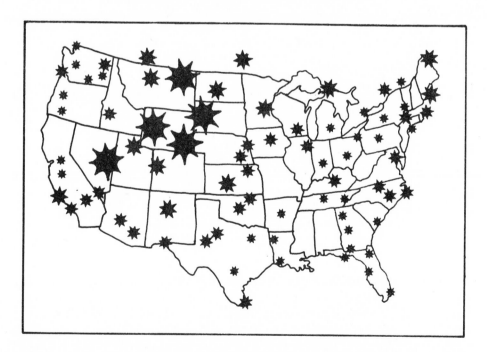

Figure II-9. *Varied suitability of areas for solar heating based on available sunshine and local heating needs — larger sun symbols indicate more favorable conditions* (from Ames *Iowa Daily Tribune,* April 6, 1979)

CLIMATE

References

1. *Guide to Solar Energy Programs,* 061-00-00042-9, U.S. Dept. of Energy, Washington, D.C., June 1978.
2. *Minimum Property Standards for Solar Heating,* Vol. 5, Dept. of Housing & Urban Development, Washington, D.C., 1977.
3. Roger R. Getz and Michael M. Nicholas, *Probabilities and Extremes of Solar Radiation by Climatic Week,* National Weather Service Technical Memorandum SR-98, National Oceanic and Atmospheric Administration, Washington, D.C., 1979.
4. Robert J. List, *Smithsonian Meteorological Tables,* p. 501 (adapted from *Heating and Ventilation,* Vol. 45, 1948, p. 86).
5. *ASHRAE Handbook and Product Directory, Applications,* p. 593, American Society of Heating, Refrigeration and Air-Conditioning Engineers, New York, 1974.
6. "Available Solar Radiation at the Surface," Ames *Iowa Daily Tribune,* April 6, 1979.

III. SOLAR TECHNOLOGY

Solar energy systems absorb solar radiation, convert it to a more convenient form of energy, and either use it at once or store it for later delivery to the point of use when needed (Figure III-1). A system may include an auxiliary energy source to maintain the supply when available solar radiation is not sufficient to meet requirements.

Systems without storage or an auxiliary energy source, for example, flat-plate solar collectors that preheat normal ventilation air in a livestock structure as the solar energy is received, are usually much cheaper to build and maintain than more complex systems with additional components. However, such a limited system will meet a smaller fraction of the building heat requirements with solar energy.

Often, one system component may perform several functions simultaneously. One example is a masonry wall of a livestock building that can collect, convert, and store solar energy.

Solar energy systems are categorized as passive or active. A passive system depends on natural convection, conduction, or radiation to transfer thermal energy from the point of collection to the storage component and to the point of use. The points of collection and use in a passive system frequently coincide. An active system has mechanical means such as a pump or fan to drive a heat-transfer fluid from one part of the system to another. Components are generally more complex than those of a passive system and controllers and circuits may be needed to regulate system operation.

Many agricultural applications such as greenhouses, field drying of crops, and warming of roof-mounted water tanks, use passive solar systems. With proper building orientation and roof overhang, a curtain-sided poultry house may be passively heated (Figure III-2). During winter months, when the sun is low in the sky, solar radiation bathes the south wall. The curtain wall absorbs part of the radiation and conducts heat to the inside of the house where the air distributes it by convection. Since most curtain materials are partially transparent, they transmit some radiation which is then absorbed in the interior of the house. During the summer months, when the sun is high, the roof overhang shades the south wall against direct radiation, thus avoiding unwanted heating in hot weather.

Active solar systems have been used for decades and have proved feasible in many parts of the world. However, more development is necessary before large-scale application can become a reality. The material that follows deals primarily with components of active solar energy systems adaptable for agricultural enterprises.[1-6]

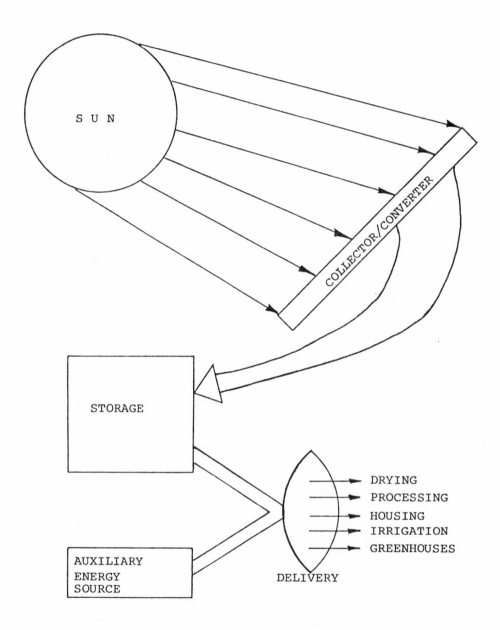

Figure III-1. *Schematic of solar energy system*

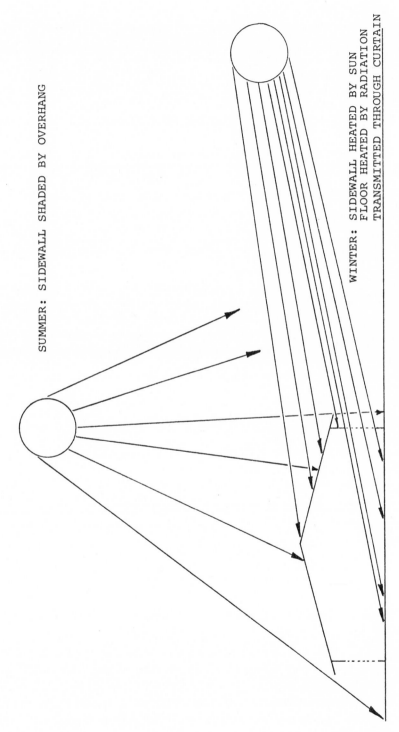

SUMMER: SIDEWALL SHADED BY OVERHANG

WINTER: SIDEWALL HEATED BY SUN
FLOOR HEATED BY RADIATION
TRANSMITTED THROUGH CURTAIN

Figure III-2. *Passive heating of poultry house*

Thermal Collectors

Solar energy collectors absorb solar radiation and convert it into heat or electricity. They can be categorized as low or high temperature collectors depending on whether they operate below or above 115°C (approximately 240°F). Low temperature units are mostly flat-plate or evacuated-tube types (the evacuated-tube design is a special case of the flat plate). Since the absorbing surface is flat, it can receive both direct and diffuse radiation. High temperature units are concentrating or focusing collectors. Since they bring together parallel incoming rays to create higher intensity, they operate on direct radiation. Although the flat-plate, evacuated-tube, and concentrating collectors are the most common, a wide variety of other designs have been used.

Thermal collectors have also been constructed of many different materials. For agricultural applications in particular, the choice of materials, together with considerations of basic design, installation procedures, and operating conditions, should make care and maintenance simple and easy. They should minimize such problems as breakage of glazing due to mismatched thermal expansions, deterioration of paint on absorber surfaces, freezing of heat-transfer fluids, accumulation of moisture inside the collector, deposits of dust or other foreign matter on the collection surface, and corrosion of pipes by reaction with the atmosphere or heat-transfer fluids.

Low-Temperature Collectors

A typical low-temperature collector, shown schematically in Figure III-3, has five basic components: an absorber plate, a heat-transfer fluid and fluid passage, a transparent cover or glazing, insulation, and an enclosure. The essentials are the same for flat-plate and evacuated-tube types.

Heat Transfer Fluid. The heat-transfer fluid is considered first because the choice of fluid can influence the character of other collector components. Both liquid and air are used extensively in agricultural applications to remove heat from the collector. Which fluid is more suitable depends on the end use of the collected energy and the type of storage, if any.

Air has obvious advantages for such applications as crop drying and confinement house ventilation which require large amounts of heated air. The air to be heated can circulate through the collector and/or the storage system, eliminating the need for a separate heat exchanger, reducing losses, and improving efficiency. Air does not freeze to rupture pipes and valves. Although air leaks reduce the system efficiency and are more difficult than liquid leaks to locate and repair, liquid leaks present more serious problems.

Liquids offer advantages in other applications. For example, when the desired end product is hot water, water is the choice for a heat-transfer fluid. Although other liquids have been used in various applications, water is most common. Problems include corrosion and damage to surroundings by freezing or leaks.

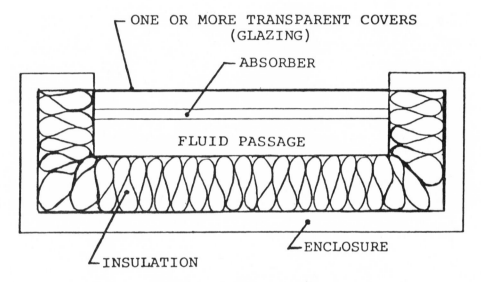

ONE OR MORE TRANSPARENT COVERS
(GLAZING)

ABSORBER

FLUID PASSAGE

INSULATION

ENCLOSURE

Figure III-3. *Basic flat-plate collector*

Corrosion can be controlled by making plumbing of non-corroding materials such as copper, glass, and polyvinyl chloride or by adding corrosion inhibitors to the water. Inhibitors usually require a double-walled heat exchanger between the collector and delivery circuits because most inhibitors are toxic and may be too expensive for use as storage media. They also create a disposal problem when the system must be drained.

Freezing can be prevented by the addition of an antifreeze such as ethylene glycol to the water. However, glycol solutions present problems similar to those associated with corrosion inhibitors and also break down at the high temperatures encountered during stagnation. Hydrocarbon oils or silicone fluids that are stable at high temperatures can also be used, but do not transfer heat as efficiently as do glycols.

A drain-down collector system can protect against freezing without chemical additives. In such a system, shown in Figure III-4, all the water exposed to freezing temperatures in the collector and plumbing drains back into the storage tank when the collector pumps are turned off. Collectors must be drainable, pipes must be

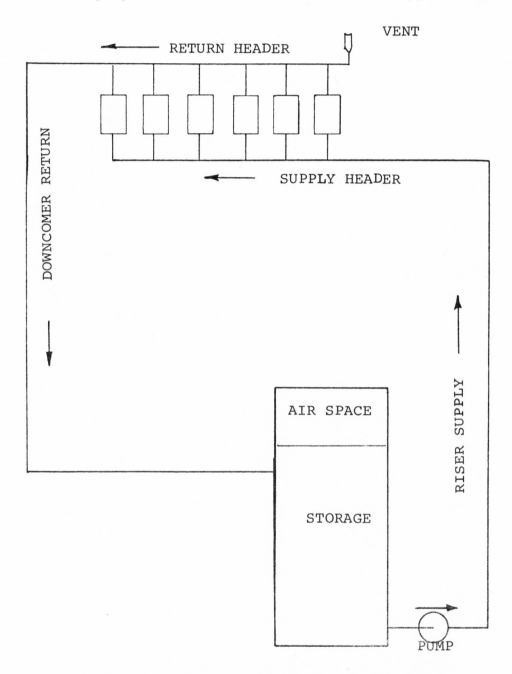

Figure III-4. *Drain-down system to prevent freezing of heat-transfer liquid*

pitched to ensure complete gravity drainage, and the temperature of all pipes situated below the water level in the storage tank must be above freezing. The highest point of the return header must be vented to relieve the vacuum left behind by the draining water on shutdown and to allow the escape of air displaced by incoming water on startup. The vent may open to the atmosphere or to the head space at the top of the storage tank. Head space must be large enough to allow all the water to drain from the collector and the supply and return lines into the storage tank.

Absorber. The absorber intercepts solar radiation, absorbs as much as possible, converts it to heat, and passes the heat on to the transfer fluid. Commercially manufactured collectors are commonly made of copper, aluminum, or steel, but inexpensive collectors for agricultural applications have been homemade of such materials as wood, black plastic, building felt, and painted rocks. If the heat-transfer fluid is a liquid, the collector must usually be made of metal, but any solid material is suitable with air.

A heat-transfer liquid requires passages to confine and direct its motion, especially if the system is to be pressurized. The liquid passages are usually tubes integral to the absorber or attached to the upper or lower absorber surface as in Figure III-5.

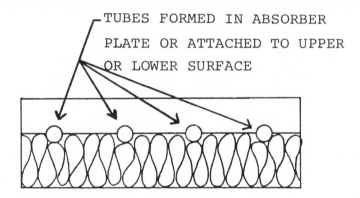

TUBES FORMED IN ABSORBER
PLATE OR ATTACHED TO UPPER
OR LOWER SURFACE

Figure III-5. *Typical flat-plate collector with tubular channels for heat-transfer liquid*

Care must be taken to achieve a good thermal bond to facilitate heat transfer from the absorber to the tubes. Poorly clamped or badly soldered tubes can reduce the effective absorber surface to that of the tubes alone.

When the heat-transfer fluid is air, it is usually allowed to contact the entire absorber surface as in Figure III-3. The air may flow the length of the collector between the cover plate and the upper absorber face and then make a return pass underneath the absorber before leaving the collector. Figures III-6 through III-8 show other absorber configurations for air heaters.

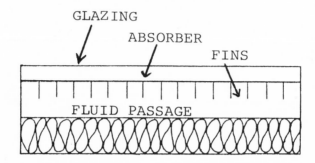

Figure III-6. *Finned-plate absorber*

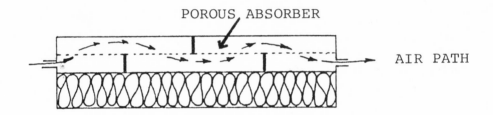

Figure III-7. *Porous absorber*

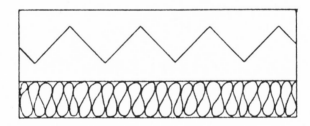

Figure III-8. *V-corrugated absorber*

The ability of an absorber to usefully capture solar radiation is expressed as its absorptance (primarily in the shortwave solar spectrum from 0.3 to 3.0 micrometers). Absorptance is the fraction of incident radiation that is absorbed and varies from 0 for a perfect reflector to 1 for an ideal black body. Its value depends on the character and configuration of the absorber surface. The V-corrugation of the absorber in Figure III-8 has a greater absorptance than a plane with the same intrinsic surface character because incoming rays can undergo multiple reflections before escaping. More absorption occurs each time a reflected ray strikes another part of the absorber surface.

V-corrugations have two other advantages. They increase the area of contact between the heated absorber surface and the air transfer fluid so that heat flow is more rapid, and they are selective in that they increase the absorptance more than they do the emittance. Emittance is the ratio of the heat radiated away from a surface to that radiated from an ideal black body at the same temperature. A smaller rise in emittance means a smaller increase in the heat lost by reradiation away from the warm absorber.

·Most absorber surfaces are treated to increase absorption. The most common and usually most economical treatment is a coating of flat black paint which can raise the absorptance to about 0.9. It is also possible to improve absorber efficiency with selective coatings which enhance absorption of shortwave radiation from the sun (hotter objects radiate at shorter wavelengths) but not emission of longwave radiation from the absorber (the absorber is much cooler than the sun and therefore radiates heat at much longer wavelengths, from about 3.0 to 30 micrometers). Figure III-9 shows the variation of reflectance with wavelength for a common selective coating, black chrome. At short wavelengths (solar radiation), black chrome is a

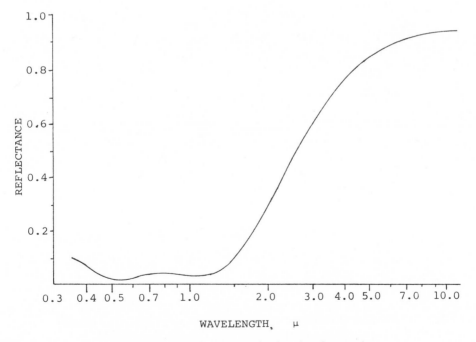

Figure III-9. *Black-chrome selective absorber coating*

poor reflector, that is, a good absorber. (As a good absorber, it is also a good emitter, but this has no significance here because the absorber emits very little radiation at the short wavelengths.) For long wavelengths (radiation losses from the absorber surface), it is a good reflector, that is, a poor emitter (and absorber).

Selective surfaces become more important the higher the absorber surface temperature rises above that of the surrounding air. As Figure III-10 shows, when the temperature difference between the absorber and the air is relatively small, or the incident radiation is relatively high, black paint and black chrome are about equally efficient. The selective black chrome coating is significantly superior only when the temperature difference is relatively large compared with the incident radiation. Since most collectors for agricultural purposes operate at relatively low temperatures, use of the more costly black chrome coating is rarely warranted.

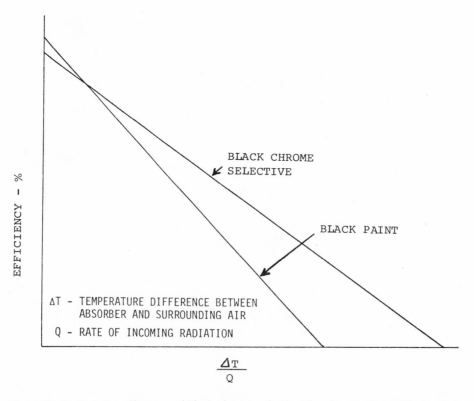

Figure III-10. *Relative efficiency of black-chrome selective absorber coating vs black paint*

Glazing. The primary purpose of glazing as a collector cover is the reduction of heat losses from the upper surface of the absorber plate. Secondarily, glazing also protects against bad weather and prolongs the absorber life.

Glass has been the principal material used for glazing, but plastic films of such compositions as Teflon, Tedlar, Lexan, Mylar W, polyvinyl chloride, and polyethylene have also been used. Plastics are generally less expensive than glass, resist shatter and impact damage, are easy to cut and shape for on-site collector fabrication, have low weight per unit surface area, and are easy to repair or replace if damaged. However, plastics also have such disadvantages as high temperature coefficients of expansion, loss of strength at high temperatures, and reduced transparency with prolonged exposure to ultraviolet radiation. Mylar W, polyvinyl chloride, and polyethylene are suitable only for low temperature applications, and the latter two materials require yearly replacement.

Fiberglass-reinforced plastics like those used in greenhouses have also been applied successfully to collector glazing. However, some of these materials degrade rapidly at the elevated temperatures in solar collectors. The Kalwall Corporation makes a fiberglass-reinforced polyester specifically for glazing solar collectors, and other manufacturers will undoubtedly enter this market as the use of solar energy becomes more widespread.

Although glazing effectively reduces convective losses from the absorber, it also reflects and absorbs some of the incident solar radiation (Figure III-11), thus reduc-

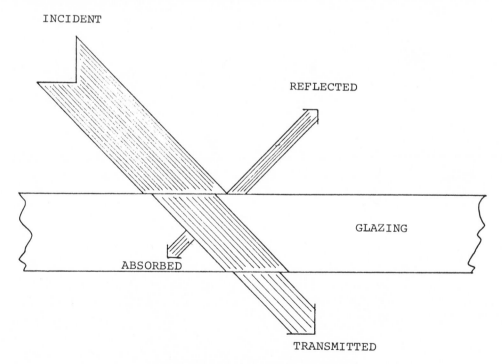

Figure III-11. *Glazing radiation losses*

ing the amount that reaches the absorber surface. Glass has the highly desirable property of transmitting about 90% of incident shortwave solar radiation[1] while transmitting virtually no longwave (thermal) radiation from the absorber. On the other hand, plastics may transmit as much as 40% of the absorber radiation, increasing system heat losses, and are generally not as transparent as glass to the sun's rays.

Transmittance of direct radiation varies significantly with the angle of incidence, as shown in Figure III-12 for low-iron glass. The transmittance for this glass begins

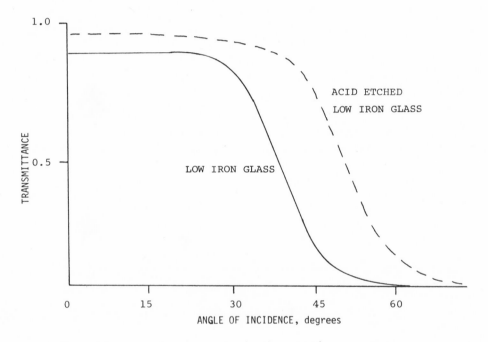

Figure III-12. *Effect of surface treatment on variation of glass transmittance with angle of incidence of radiation*

to decrease sharply when the angle of incidence rises above about 30 degrees.[7] A special acid etching of the surface not only increases the transmittance, but also shifts the critical angle upward to about 45 degrees. Acid-etched glass may not be readily available, but a more easily obtained glass with a stippled or matte finish has a transmittance somewhere between that of smooth and acid-etched glasses. Other surface treatments such as anti-reflective coatings improve transmission, but are prohibitively expensive.

Accumulations of dust and dirt on the glazing surface reduce the amount of incident radiation transmitted to the absorber. In residential and commercial environments, natural washing by rain is generally considered sufficient to maintain adequate transmission. This may not be the case for the greater quantities of dust in agricultural environments. Also, airborne organic matter like that discharged from a crop dryer or livestock housing unit can become glued to the glazing surface and significantly degrade transmittance.

   Multiple glazing is a common means of further reducing convective heat loss from the absorber. Although it does do so, it also reduces transmission of incident radiation by the addition of more reflecting and absorbing surfaces. The net result may be less rather than more efficiency, as shown in Figure III-13. Since most agricultural applications of solar energy require relatively low temperatures, convective heat loss from the absorbers is also relatively low. Multiple glazing is usually not necessary or even desirable, and the added expense is not warranted. Single glazing will normally be sufficient.

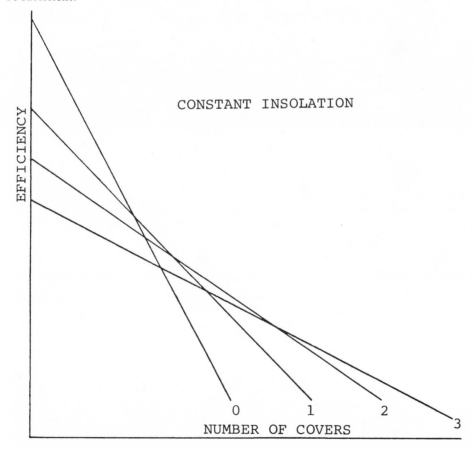

Figure III-13. *Effect of multiple glazing on collector efficiency*

Insulation. Insulation helps to ensure that a large percentage of the collected heat is passed from the absorber to the heat-transfer fluid rather than lost to the surroundings.. The insulating value per unit mass and per unit volume should be high, and the insulating materials should withstand the highest temperature that may occur in the collectors. Stagnation temperatures over 149°C (300°F) are not uncommon during periods of high incident solar radiation when the heat-transfer fluid is not being pumped through the collector.

Fiberglass and closed-cell foams are probably the most prevalent insulation in agricultural solar collectors. Fiberglass is more stable than the foams at high temperatures, but can lose its insulating ability if it becomes wet. Liquid can leak into the insulation from rain or from heat-transfer liquids. In air-heating collectors, moisture from the air may condense in the insulation.

Enclosures. Enclosures protect against dust, moisture, and other atmospheric elements, and also give strength and rigidity to collectors. Primary considerations are cost and availability of enclosure materials, ease of fabrication, resistance to corrosion and mechanical damage, weight, and compatibility with other materials used in the collector. Commercially manufactured units are generally made of aluminum or sheet steel, but wood is popular for user-built collectors common in agricultural applications. Tools and expertise for working with wood are available on most farms, but sheet-metal skills may not be.

Evacuated Tubes. The efficiency of a flat-plate collector decreases for higher absorber operating temperatures because a greater difference between the absorber and surrounding temperatures usually causes greater heat losses. A major portion of the heat losses are due to convection from the absorber to the cover and then to the surroundings. A simple means to reduce this loss is to enclose the absorber and fluid passage in an evacuated transparent tube as shown in Figure III-14. The absence of air between the absorber and the transparent tube wall prevents convection so that heat losses are reduced to thermal radiation alone. Increased efficiency makes absorber temperatures of 120–260°C (250–500°F) attainable with resulting increases in energy output. The improved performance of evacuated-tube collectors is accomplished without the loss of ability to capture diffuse radiation as occurs with focusing collectors discussed below.

Although the evacuated-tube collector is also more efficient than the ordinary flat-plate type at lower operating temperatures, its advantage is diminished by the lower energy output. Collector cost per unit collected energy then makes the ordinary flat plate more cost-effective than the evacuated tube. Most agricultural applications of solar energy will not require the high-temperature performance capability of an evacuated tube.

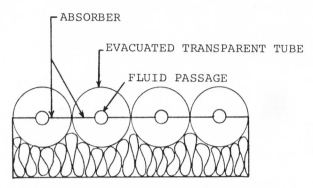

Figure III-14. *Evacuated-tube collector*

High-Temperature Collectors

When required temperatures exceed about 121°C (250°F), the intensity of the solar radiation striking the absorber surface must be increased. This can be done with reflecting surfaces or lenses which focus the radiation on a small area. The simple form of focusing collector shown in Figure III-15 consists of a parabolic trough

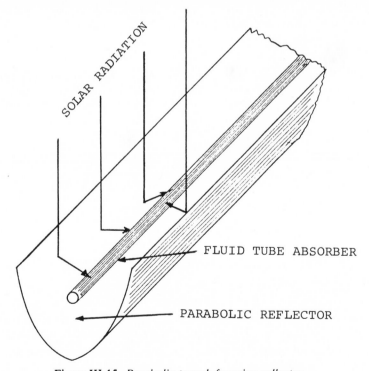

Figure III-15. *Parabolic-trough focusing collector*

(paraboloid) with a reflective coating on its inner surface and an absorber-fluid tube mounted along the focal line. Concentration ratios of 30–50 are not uncommon.

Unlike flat-plate designs, concentrating collectors work only with the direct rays from the sun. They are effective only when the major portion of incident solar energy is available as direct radiation.

Figures III-16 and III-17 show other configurations for concentrating collectors. The central-receiver absorber of Figure III-17, surrounded by a field of mirrors, can attain concentration ratios up to 1000 and temperatures up to 538°C (1000°F). These temperatures are useful primarily to generate steam. The steam can then be used directly in food and feed processing or to drive electric generators that supply power to large electric motors like those found in irrigation systems or feed mills.

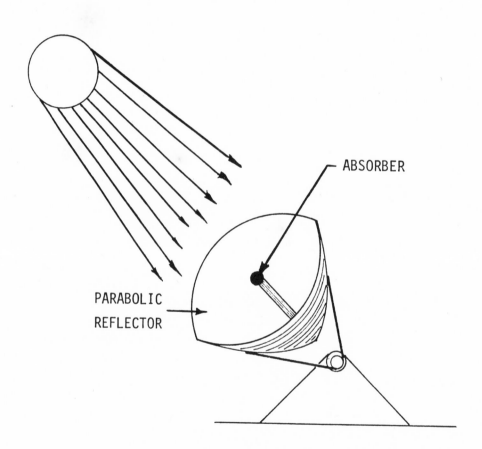

ABSORBER

PARABOLIC
REFLECTOR

Figure III-16. *Paraboloidal-dish focusing collector*

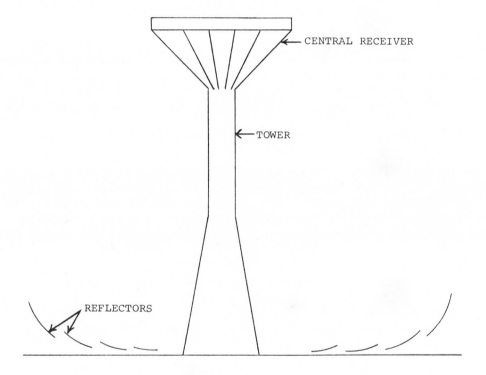

Figure III-17. *Central-receiver focusing collector system*

Since concentrating collectors depend primarily on direct radiation, they must always face the sun. The parabolic trough can be oriented with its axis running east-west and then will require approximately weekly adjustment only for changes in the sun's declination. However, the orientation of the paraboloidal dish and central-receiver systems requires daily correction for declination and must also track the sun as it moves across the sky from east to west.

Costs for dish and central-receiver systems are high because these systems demand precision in manufacturing and construction to function efficiently and must include means for adjusting their orientation. Dimensional tolerances must be close to ensure that the collected radiation is focused exactly on the absorber-receiver.

Photovoltaic Collectors

The photovoltaic effect, generation of an electric voltage by light falling on a suitable material, has been known for over 100 years. However, its practical application to the conversion of solar energy has developed primarily during the last two decades, notably in electric power supplies on spacecraft.

The photovoltaic effect takes place when light (or other electromagnetic radiation) interacts with a thin layer of semiconducting material and frees electric charges to flow in an external circuit. Electric energy is generated only while light is striking the photosensitive material. The electricity must be used to charge a battery or energize some other storage device if the energy is to be stored for later consumption.

Many semiconductor materials display the photovoltaic effect, but vary in efficiency. The maximum theoretical efficiency of a single solar cell is 25%[8], and commercial units do not achieve this level. Relatively low efficiency and high cost have retarded the wide use of these devices.

Agricultural applications of photovoltaic collectors are very limited at present. As efficiencies rise and costs fall, more applications may become practical, for example, driving electric motors in irrigation systems. In the near term, photovoltaic collectors may serve as power supplies for motors and associated controls in remote locations where connection to conventional power lines or the use of engine-driven generators is not economically feasible.

Storage

The energy requirements of an agricultural enterprise can vary with the time of day, the day of the year, and the elapsed time since the start of an energy-consuming process. An excellent example is the heat required for brooding broiler chickens.

Flood et al[9] found that approximately 60% of the average daily heat requirement was used at night between 6 PM and 6 AM (Figure III-18). Note that this is a period when no solar energy is available. For the grow-out period, 12 times as much heat was needed during the colder first calendar quarter than during the warmer third quarter. Also, the daily heat requirement is 6 times greater at the beginning than at the end of the first 4 weeks of the 8-week production period.

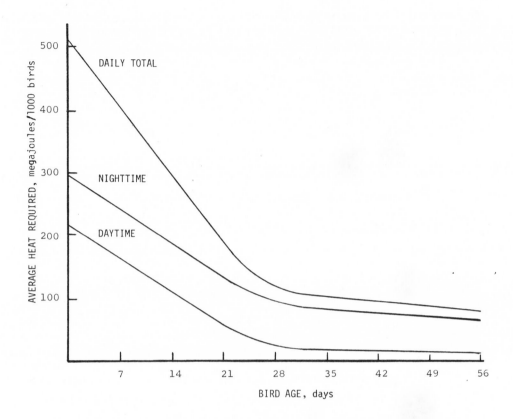

Figure III-18. *Typical heat requirements for brooding broiler breeders*

On the other hand, available solar radiation varies in intensity with the time of day, the season of the year, weather, and geography. Obviously, supply and demand will rarely coincide exactly. To better match them, solar energy must be stored for later use.

Energy storage can have a thermal, chemical, mechanical, or electrical form. It can be the product of some intermediate process, for example, distilled water or a regenerated desiccant. It can consist of retrievable potential energy in liquid elevated by a solar-energy-powered pump. Storage possibilities are limited only by the imagination of the system designer. However, the type and quantity of storage must be compatible with other components of the system, with the form and level of energy requirements, and with the availability of solar radiation.

Sensible Heat Storage

The most common means of storing solar energy is as sensible heat in a liquid or solid. Sensible heat is the kind that raises the temperature of a substance as opposed to latent heat of fusion, for example, which changes a solid into a liquid without a temperature rise. The quantity of sensible heat that can be stored in a given amount of liquid or solid is:

$$Q = mc\Delta T$$

where: Q is the quantity of heat stored

        m is the mass of storage substance

        c is the specific heat of the substance

        ΔT is the increase in temperature

The amount of storage substance needed is calculated on the basis of the amount of energy the system must store to meet load requirements and the allowable or attainable temperature limits.

Specific heat indicates the relative ability of a mass of particular substance to store energy. However, the volume of the mass may be more significant because the space available for energy storage may be a more serious limitation than weight restrictions. A volumetric comparison of storage materials is based on the relationship:

$$q = \varrho c\Delta T$$

where: q is the heat stored per unit volume

        ϱ is the density (mass/volume) of the storage material

The product ϱc expresses the heat stored per unit volume per degree temperature rise, that is, the relative volumetric heat-storage ability. Other considerations, such as temperature limits, cost, convenience, stability, and maintenance, being equal, a designer would select storage materials with high values of ϱc because they require the least space to store a given amount of heat. Table III-1 lists data for various materials suitable for sensible heat storage. Note that water has the highest heat capacity of the group, about three times that of crushed rocks.

Complete analysis of storage performance requires consideration of the relation of storage to other system components, including heat loss to the surroundings.

Table III-1. Thermal capacity of storage materials

Material	Specific Heat, C		Heat Capacity, ϱC		Density, ϱ	
	cal/g-°C	kJ/kg-°C	Btu/ft³-°C	kJ/m³-°C	lb/ft³	kg/m³
Water	1.00	4.19	62.4	4190	62.4	1000
Water-ethylene glycol 30:70 mixture by weight @ 230°F	0.80	3.35	51.3	3440	64.0	1025
Concrete	0.156	0.654	22.5	1510	144	2310
Scrap iron	0.12	0.50	53.9	3620	451	7230
Rocks (crushed)	0.20	0.84	20.0	1340	100	1601
Marble (solid)	0.21	0.88	34.1	2290	162	2600
Rock salt	0.219	0.918	29.8	2000	136	2180
Sand	0.191	0.800	18.3	1230	95.7	1533
Stone (quarried)	0.20	0.84	19.2	1290	96.2	1540

During a period when energy is being collected and heat is being partly delivered for end use and partly added to storage, as shown in Figure III-19, the instantaneous condition can be expressed as:

$$Q_c = Q_u + Q_s + Q_l$$

where: Q_c is the rate at which the collector is producing heat

Q_u is the rate at which useful energy is being delivered for end use

Q_s is the rate at which heat is being added to storage

Q_l is the rate at which heat is being lost to the surroundings

That is, the heat flow from the collector divides along three paths, one to the user, one to storage, and one to losses or waste. Rewriting the equation in terms of the useful energy flow:

$$Q_u = Q_c - Q_s - Q_l$$

To maximize the delivery of useful energy, Q_u, waste should be minimized and preferably made small compared with Q_u, Q_c, and Q_s.

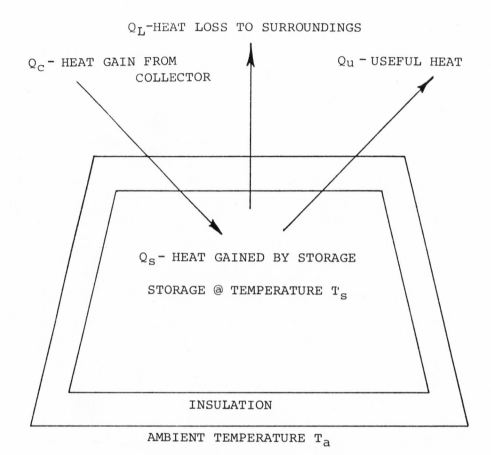

Q_L–HEAT LOSS TO SURROUNDINGS

Q_c – HEAT GAIN FROM
            COLLECTOR

Q_u – USEFUL HEAT

Q_s – HEAT GAINED BY STORAGE

STORAGE @ TEMPERATURE T'_s

INSULATION

AMBIENT TEMPERATURE T_a

Figure III-19. *Storage heat balance*

The rate at which heat is being lost can be expressed as:

$$Q_1 = AU(T_s - T_a)$$

where: A is the storage surface area

U is the overall heat transfer coefficient (rate of heat loss per unit storage surface area)

T_s is the average storage temperature

T_a is the ambient temperature of the storage surroundings

The storage designer reduces heat losses primarily by making A and U small, selecting a container shape with a small ratio of surface area to volume and surrounding it with adequate insulation. Typical shapes are spheres, cubes, and cylinders with diameters equal to their heights. The justifiable amount of insulation is determined by balancing insulation cost against the value of lost heat.

Heat loss varies with the difference $T_s - T_a$. When storage is above ground and exposed to atmospheric conditions, temperature differences will vary over a wide range. Losses will be greater in winter than in summer. If winter is a season of major energy use, the designer should primarily consider winter losses in calculating insulation requirements.

On the other hand, if storage is below ground, losses will remain relatively constant over all seasons. Insulation will still be required, but will be based on the expectation of a relatively constant ground temperature at any given location. The ground is also a good heat absorber, that is, it has a high heat capacity particularly when wet due to a high water table or other source of ground water.

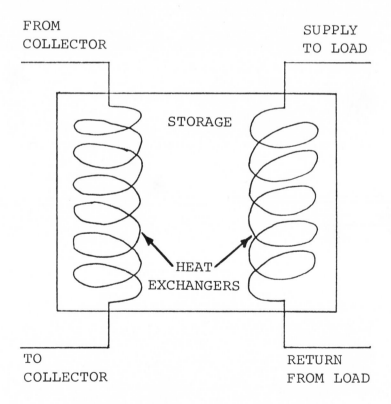

Figure III-20. *Liquid storage with heat exchangers*

Liquids. Water is the most widely used liquid storage medium. It is inexpensive, readily available, and easily disposed of when drainage is necessary. It is also the obvious choice for storage if it is also the heat-transfer fluid or hot water is the desired end product of the solar heating process. Factors discussed for heat-transfer fluids apply also to storage media.

Plumbing arrangements vary according to specific requirements. Figure III-20 shows a system suitable for separating both the collector and delivery circuits from the storage liquid and from each other. This is necessary, for example, if antifreeze, a corrosion inhibitor, or a special-heat transfer fluid is used in the collector circuit and must be prevented from entering the delivery circuit. In this system, the storage liquid does not leave the storage tank.

If separation of circuits is not necessary, either or both heat exchangers can be removed from the system. If the collector is a drain-down type, the heat exchanger in the collector circuit is usually omitted while the delivery exchanger is retained to permit the delivery circuit to be pressurized. The pressurized delivery circuit is then continuously filled with liquid. In the most common arrangement for agricultural applications, neither heat exchanger is present and the storage liquid circulates through both the collector and delivery circuits.

When the storage volume is large compared with the liquid flow rates at inlets and outlets, it is possible to establish and maintain temperature stratification in the storage tank as shown in Figure III-21. Since the density of most liquids decreases as their temperature increases, hot liquid rises to the top and cold liquid falls to the bottom of the tank. In operation, cold liquid is drawn from the bottom of the tank and pumped through the collector where it is heated and then flows back into the top of

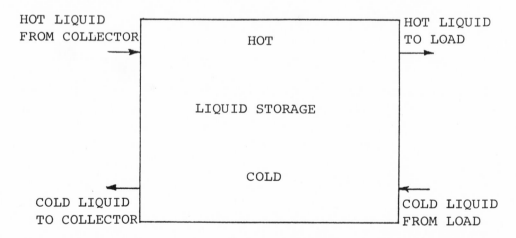

Figure III-21. *Stratified-temperature storage*

the tank. On the delivery side, hot liquid is drawn from the top of the tank and cold liquid returns to the bottom. If entrance and exit liquid velocities are relatively high, turbulent flow will mix the liquid in the storage tank and destroy the stratification.

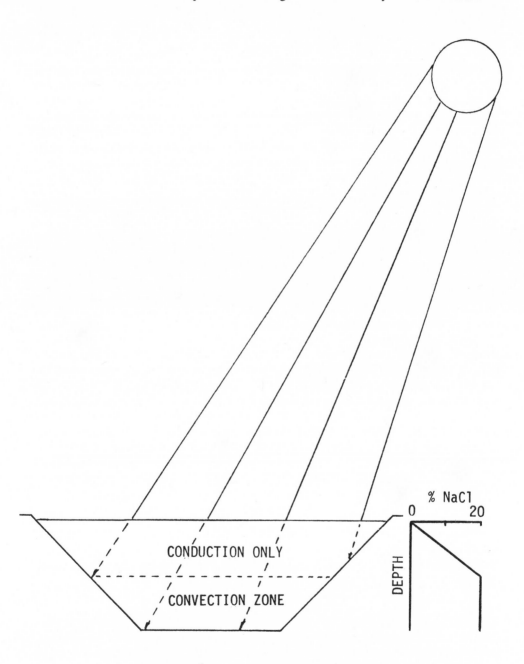

Figure III-22. *Saline-pond solar collector/storage*

With collector and delivery heat exchangers separating the circuits, the liquid in the storage tank is stagnant so that temperature stratification occurs naturally. However, when heat exchangers are absent, and inlet and outlet velocities are low, stratification is more readily established because the collector and delivery liquid flows reinforce the temperature gradient.

Stratification of storage temperature has two major advantages. First, the temperature of the liquid pumped out of the bottom of the storage tank into the collector is colder than it would be if the storage liquid were well mixed. Since the rate at which heat passes from absorber to liquid in the collector is proportional to their temperature difference, a colder liquid will pick up more heat and improve the collector efficiency. Second, more heat will be delivered to the user because the liquid leaving the top outlet will be hotter than if the storage liquid were well mixed.

The saline pond in Figure III-22 is a combination collector-storage liquid system that can be used for long-term storage.[11] It is heated by absorption of shortwave solar radiation throughout its depth and at the pond liner. Most longer-wave infrared radiation is absorbed only near the pond surface and its heat contribution is lost by evaporation and convection to the air. Since the pond is transparent to intermediate-wavelength visible and ultraviolet radiation, these wavelengths are absorbed primarily by the lower portion of the pond and by the liner.

By addition of salt, a high-density saline zone is established in the lower portion of the pond. The high salt concentration of approximately 20% diminishes linearly above this zone to 0% at the pond's surface. Near the pond's bottom, convection currents transfer heat absorbed by the pond's liner to the salt water. The constant concentration gradient in the upper part of the pond prevents convection from circulating pond water so that heat remains stored in the high-density saline zone. Heat is then lost through the upper zone to the surface only by conduction. Since conduction is a much slower transfer process than the convection that would exist in the absence of the salt concentration gradient, heat losses are much smaller. The saline pond can be used to collect and store heat during the summer for use during the winter.

Solids. A loosely packed bed of material such as rocks can serve as a storage medium. Such beds are often used when air is the heat-transfer fluid circulated through the collector. Table III-1 lists the heat capacities of some commonly used solid storage materials.[10]

Figure III-23 shows the operation of a typical rock storage. Heat is stored by circulating hot air from the collector through the rocks and then back to the collector to pick up more heat. Heat is delivered by circulating air in the reverse direction through the rocks, where it is uniformly heated, and then into the delivery circuit.

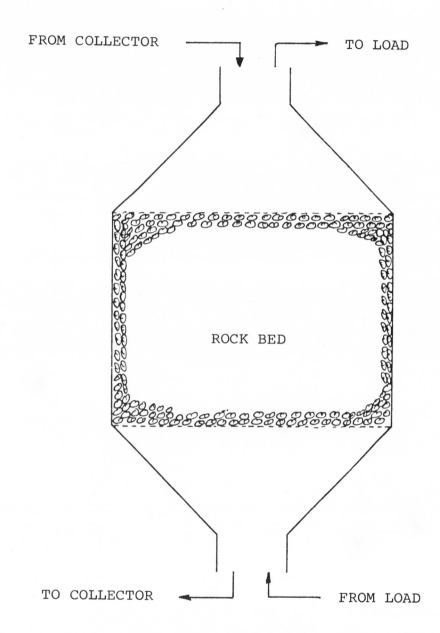

Figure III-23. *Rock-bed heat storage*

With this arrangement, heat cannot be simultaneously replenished from the collector and delivered to the load. A bypass system that directs some of the air from the collector to the delivery circuit permits such simultaneous operation.

Since the heat-transfer coefficient between air and rocks is high, the hot air entering the inlet to the storage quickly raises the temperature of the first rocks it touches
and the rocks and air rapidly reach equilibrium. Because the rocks cannot mix to
distribute the heat as a liquid storage medium can, the temperature stratifies across
the rock bed. Bed temperature will be close to that of collector air at the inlet and
close to that of air returning from the load at the outlet.

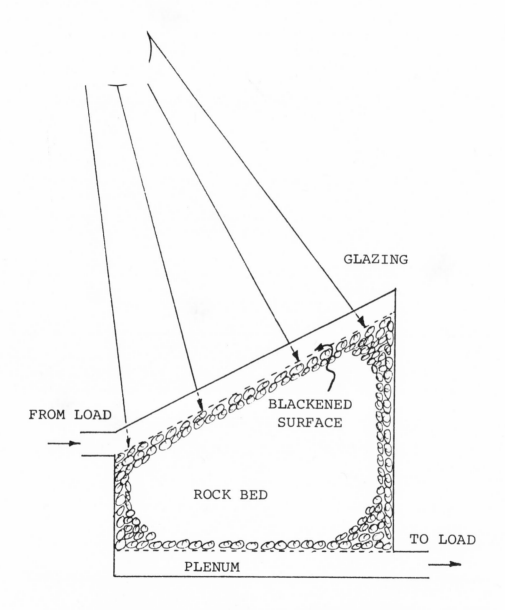

Figure III-24. *Combination collector and rock-bed storage*

Rocks are poor thermal conductors so that temperature differences disappear slowly when air is not moving through the bed. Insulation requirements for rock beds are not as demanding as for liquid storage because conduction losses from rocks are much less than the combined convective-conductive losses from liquids.

Combination collector-storage systems using rock beds are common. Figure III-24 shows a simple example. The rock bed, with its upper surface painted black and covered by glazing, is situated over a plenum. Air drawn in between the glazing and the black surface flows through the rock bed into the plenum. Auxiliary ducting, fans, and controls allow the circulation of the air through the bed and back to the absorbing surface whenever solar radiation is available but the load requires no heat, or through the load when heat is demanded. A system with secondary recirculation and an absorber plate over the rock bed (Figure III-25) permits simultaneous collection and delivery.

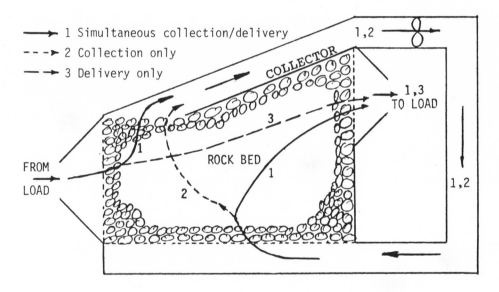

Figure III-25. *Rock-bed storage/collector with recirculation*

Phase-Change Storage

Phase-change storage takes advantage of the latent heat of fusion absorbed when a solid melts to become liquid or the latent heat of vaporization when a liquid changes to a vapor (gas). The latent heat should be large, the phase change should occur at a temperature suitable for the application, and the change should be repeatedly reversible for a long time without deterioration of the storage medium.

It is also desirable that very little volume change accompany the phase change. This requirement favors the solid-liquid transition because most substances increase in volume by several orders of magnitude when changing from liquid to vapor at constant pressure. The liquid-vapor transition is unsuitable for most storage applications.

Table III-2. Phase-change thermal energy storage materials

Materials	Melting point		Heat of fusion		Heat capacity	
	°F	°C	Btu/lb	kJ/kg	Btu/ft³	kJ/m
Salt hydrates						
$Na_2SO_4 \cdot \frac{1}{2}NH_4Cl \cdot \frac{1}{2}NaCl \cdot 10H_2O$	55	12.8	78	181	7200	268,265
$K_2HPO_4 \cdot 6H_2O$	52-56	11.1-13.3	47	109	4900	182,570
$Ca(NO_3)_2 \cdot 4H_2O$	117	47.2	66	154	7650	285,032
$Na_2S_2O_3 \cdot 5H_2O$	113-120	45.0-48.9	90	209	9200	342,784
$Na_2SO_4 \cdot 10H_2O$ (Glauber salt)	90	32.2	108	251	9900	368,865
$MgCl_2 \cdot 6H_2O$	239	115	71	165	6940	258,578
Waxes						
C14-C16 paraffin	35-45	1.7-7.2	65.4	152	3185	118,670
C15-C16 paraffin	40-50	4.4-10.0	65.7	153	3200	119,229
1-Decanol	40-45	4.4-7.2	88.6	206	4590	171,019
C14 paraffin	35-40	1.7-4.4	71.1	165	3420	127,426
C16 paraffin	58-65	14.4-18.3	86.2	200	4190	156,116
P116 paraffin	116	46.7	90	209	4380	163,195
Plastics						
High-density polyethylene	230-255	110-123.9	108	251	7200	268,266
Water	32	0	114	334	8960	333,852
Eutectic mixtures						
$CaCl_2$-$MgCl_2$-H_2O 41-10-49	77	25	75	175	---	---
$Mg(NO_3)_2 \cdot 6H_2O$-$Al(NO_3)_3 \cdot 9H_2O$ 53-47	142	61	64	148	---	---
Acetamide-stearic acid 17-83	149	65	94	218	---	---
Urea-NH_4NO_3 45.3-54.7	115	46	74	172	---	---

A number of substances such as salt hydrates, paraffins, and eutectic mixtures have melting points in a suitable range for solar energy applications. Glauber's salt ($Na_2SO_4 \cdot 10H_2O$) is one of the more common choices. Table III-2 gives data for this and other phase-change storage media.[2.10]

Hydrate salts present a major problem when repeatedly cycled through their melting point. As the salt melts, some of the hydrate releases water, producing a mixture of liquid hydrate, water containing some dissolved anhydrous salt, and some undissolved anhydrous salt. The undissolved salt crystallizes and sinks to the bottom of the storage container. On cooling back to a solid, some of the crystalline salt does not rehydrate, thus reducing the heat storage capacity. The effect is cumulative with successive cycles. Attempts to prevent such separation have not been successful. Single-component materials such as water and paraffin do not cause this problem.

A second disadvantage of phase-change heat storage materials is caused by super-cooling (cooling below the normal melting point without solidification) when heat is delivered from storage. If supercooling occurs, the latent heat of fusion may not be recovered, or it may be recovered at a significantly lower temperature with adverse effects on system performance. Addition of nucleating agents promotes normal freezing and helps to avoid supercooling.

Heat transfer to and from storage may be more troublesome with phase-change materials than with media that store sensible heat. The thermal resistance of the solid is different from that of the liquid so that the temperature difference required to add or remove heat at a given rate changes during the transition. Heat exchangers are required to separate the storage from the collector and delivery circuits as in Figure III-20.

Desiccant-regeneration Storage

Regeneration of a desiccant is an attractive means for storing solar energy used in dehydration processes such as crop drying. The regenerated desiccant removes moisture from air that is then used to dry the crop. The heat required to regenerate the desiccant can be recovered and used to preheat the drying air before it passes through the crop.

Figure III-26 shows the four steps in the desiccant regenerative drying cycle. The desiccant's "storage" capacity is its ability to absorb water between A and B. Heat derived from solar energy is added at B to raise the desiccant temperature from T_1 to T_2 and the vapor pressure of the absorbed moisture to the level of C. Air removes moisture from the desiccant, lowering the vapor pressure (but not the temperature) to the level at D. Final cooling to the starting point A (heat thus removed can be useful in preheating crop-drying air) completes regeneration. Storage capacity (water-absorption potential) does not diminish during long-term repetition of the regeneration cycle.

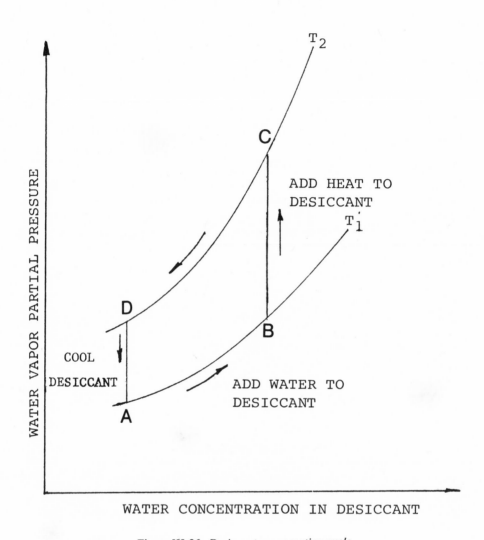

Figure III-26. *Desiccant-regeneration cycle*

Table III-3[12] summarizes the properties of several liquid desiccants and Figure III-27 illustrates a crop-drying application of desiccant-regeneration storage. The circled letters correspond to points in the desiccant-regeneration cycle of Figure III-26. Solid lines indicate air flow and dashed lines indicate desiccant flow. System variations can increase efficiency. For example, heat exchangers can be added to reclaim the heat removed from the desiccant during the final step D-A of the regenerative cycle. However, the recirculation of air through the dryer, shown in Figure III-27, may not be feasible for crops that contain a large amount of dust and other small particles.

Table III-3. Properties of liquid desiccants[12]

Desiccant	Specific heat kJ/kg°C	Relative humidity @ 32°C for solution saturation %	Useful concentration range %	Regeneration temperature range °C	Chemical stability	Heat of dilution kJ/kg	Corrosion	Toxicity
Lithium chloride	2.85 (21°C, 40% conc.)	11	23–45	95–120	Stable	~465	Relatively noncorrosive	Relatively nontoxic
Calcium chloride	2.51	21	32–40	95–120	Saturated solution solidifies below 86°F	~465	Relatively noncorrosive	None
Sulfuric acid	1.7–2.5	0	35–100	120–150	Relatively stable	~465	Very corrosive	Toxic
Glycerine (glycerol)	2.5–3.8	0	50–100	95–120	Heat sensitive, oxidizes	Low	None	None
Triethylene glycol	2.5–3.8	0	96–100	120–150	Heat sensitive	Low	Noncorrosive with inhibitor	Relatively nontoxic

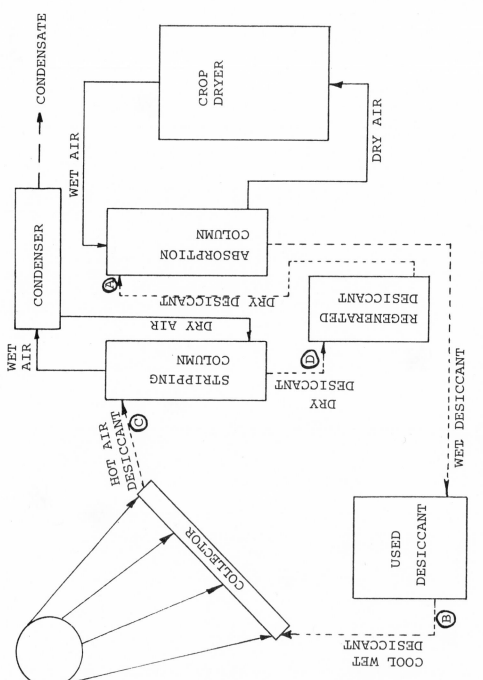

Figure III-27. *Crop drying system with desiccant storage*

Solid desiccants can also be used for storage, but not as conveniently as liquid desiccants. Solids obviously cannot be pumped through and heated directly in the solar collector. A separate heat-transfer fluid is neccessary, which can be the air used to remove moisture from the desiccant. Table III-4 lists the properties of some solid desiccants.[12]

Table III-4. Properties of solid desiccants[12]

Desiccant	Specific heat kJ/kg°C	Adsorption capacity g(H_2O)/g(desiccant)	Regeneration temperature range °C	Number of regeneration cycles	Average heat of wetting kJ/kg
Silica gel	0.84–0.92	0.4–0.5	95–170	Unlimited	∼465
Activated alumina	1.0	0.14	150–315	Unlimited	∼465
Anhydrous calcium sulfate	0.71	0.12	205–260	200 approx.	1256
Anhydrous magnesium perchlorate	Data unavailable	0.48	205–260	Limited	614
Activated carbon	0.84	0.4	105–115*	Unlimited	∼465

*For embedded heater (steam or electric).

Delivery Systems

The collected energy must be delivered to the point of use in a form and at a time suitable for the specific application. The delivery system usually consists of a heat-transfer fluid with associated ducts, pumps, controls, and, if required, an output heat exchanger. The heat-transfer fluid is normally the same type used in the collector and storage systems. Previous comments on fluids used in the collector also apply to delivery fluids.

The major component that must be specified for a delivery system is the heat exchanger or other device used to convert the stored energy to an appropriate form at the point of use. The design of these delivery units depends much more on the nature of the specific application than do the designs of the collector and storage systems. Examples are discussed in detail in Chapter IV.

Auxiliary Energy Sources

The cost of providing sufficient collector and storage capacity to meet all needs with solar energy can be prohibitive. It is usually not feasible to ensure enough storage to cope with a high-use period likely to include several consecutive days of cloudy weather. Therefore, a standby or auxiliary energy source is needed to supplement the solar system. Selection of an auxiliary energy source involves an assessment not only of cost and availability of fuels, but also of the ease of integrating the solar and auxiliary systems.

In many applications, the two systems cannot share many common components and may require two independent sets of parts. The control which senses operating conditions and switches in the appropriate energy supply may be the only element common to the two systems. When a solar energy system is added to an existing energy supply, the most cost-effective solution may be the retention of the previous supply as the auxiliary system.

Electricity is often the first choice for an auxiliary energy source because it is easy to use and control and is usually available. Natural gas is also convenient. However, a utility company may not be able to fill sudden demands for auxiliary energy when solar installations become more numerous. For example, an electric generating facility already operating near peak capacity may find it impossible to accept significant additional loads during prolonged cloudy weather from customers who normally satisfy their energy needs with sunshine. The utility may solve its problem by limiting the operation of auxiliary systems to off-peak hours when generating capacity is available. However, this requires the solar energy user to anticipate auxiliary needs so that the extra energy can be stored during these off-peak hours.

Auxiliary fuels such as coal, wood, and liquefied petroleum gas (LPG), which can be stockpiled, avoid the problem of immediate availability associated with electricity and natural gas. However, the user must provide on-site storage and may encounter seasonal variations in cost and availability. Thus, the problem of anticipating auxiliary needs becomes long rather than short term, and the user may have to order and accept delivery of fuel several months before expected use.

System Design

Design of a solar energy system can be complex. The orderly sequence includes the determination of the energy load to be supplied; the operating requirements such energy levels and supply intervals entail; the estimated size of the collector, storage, and delivery systems; the auxiliary components needed to supplement the solar system; the necessary systems controls; and finally the integrated system specifications and drawings.

Load Calculations

Estimating the times and magnitudes of energy requirements for agricultural applications may not be as simple as for residences where calculations are made from the building base heat loss and monthly degree-day averages. For example, Figure III-28 shows how the daily heat requirement for brooding broiler chickens decreases over the 8-week production cycle and varies with the time of year. During the two warmer calendar quarters, heat is needed only for the first three weeks. Earlier in this chapter, Figure III-18 showed how the required heat varied within each day, being greater at night than in daytime. Such variations are not unusual for agricultural energy use so that the successful adaptation of solar energy for such purposes requires a thorough understanding of the specific application.

Operating Requirements

Once load needs have been analyzed and calculated, decisions can be made to establish operating conditions and specifications. Decisions include:

(a) The fraction of daily and total energy requirements to be met with solar energy.

(b) Acceptable upper and lower temperature limits for the collector, storage, and delivery systems.

(c) Scheme for using auxiliary energy, for example, on demand or anticipating demand.

(d) Required number of days or hours of storage capacity.

(e) Heat-transfer fluid, storage material, and auxiliary energy source to be used.

The list (a) through (e) is not all inclusive. Rather, it is intended to stimulate thinking about the parameters involved in system development. Decisions must be specific to the application and the set goals. Examples of such goals are: minimizing unit energy cost, assuring a source for all energy requirements, and guaranteeing an energy supply for only a certain fraction of total energy needs.

Temperature requirements of the delivery system will dictate the temperature limits and perhaps the materials that can be used in the collector and storage systems. For example, peanut drying temperatures are relatively low, while the generation of power for irrigation will require high temperatures. Auxiliary system scheduling may depend on rate incentives offered by the local utility company. Operator convenience may also be a consideration. If a fuel such as coal, wood, or crop residue is burned to fire a heater, the operator may prefer to depend on auxiliary energy during the work day and fill nighttime needs with a solar-energy system which demands less supervision.

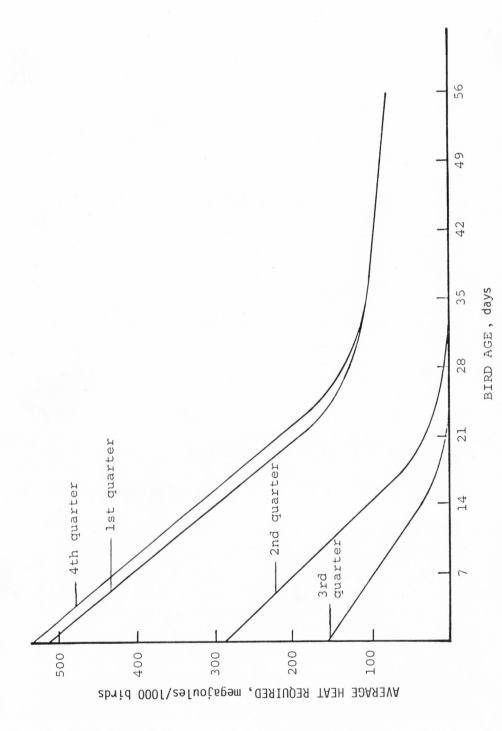

Figure III-28. *Typical average daily broiler-brooding heat requirements by calendar quarter*

Storage capacity requirements will be governed by such considerations as relative cost of collector and storage, the risk of depleting storage when solar radiation is not available, and the times when energy is needed. For example, storage with more reserve capacity may be desirable for a load like that in Figure III-28. The large storage could be charged during the last four weeks of production of one batch of birds for use and depletion during the first three or four weeks of production of the next batch. For applications with relatively constant energy needs, a storage capacity equal to a one- or two-day energy supply might be adequate.

Size of Components

After load requirements and basic system specifications have been established, determination of component size is a straightforward calculation. The total collector area is based on the amount of energy to be collected, manufacturers' data on collector performance and efficiency, and climatic tables of the availability of solar radiation. Storage volume is calculated from the required storage capacity in terms of heat and the thermal properties of the selected storage material. Capacity of the auxiliary energy system should be large enough to supply all needs if solar radiation is not available or if the solar part of the energy system fails.

Sizes of parts such as pipes, valves, pumps, and ducts are determined as for any standard heating or cooling system. When the diameters and lengths of the plumbing and details of other components are known, the work required to move fluids through the system at the desired rate should be calculated. Pumps or fans with the required flow and power ratings are then selected. Heat losses from plumbing, storage, and other parts of the system are then estimated as a function of insulation, and sufficient insulation is provided to keep the losses within acceptable limits.

Control System

Control systems may range from very simple (a human makes all decisions and actuates manual switches) to sophisticated (an elaborately programmed microcomputer automatically operates remote controls). Figure III-29 shows a typical set of controls for a basic liquid storage-heating system. A differential thermostat with two temperature sensors turns on the collector pump only when the collector temperature is about 15°C (27°F) greater than the storage temperature, and turns it off when the temperature difference falls to about 2°C (3°F). A low-limit thermostat turns on the auxiliary heating unit when the storage temperature drops below a preset minimum. A high-limit thermostat controls the delivery system and turns off the delivery pump when heat is not needed. Features of control systems vary to accommodate the needs of individual applications.

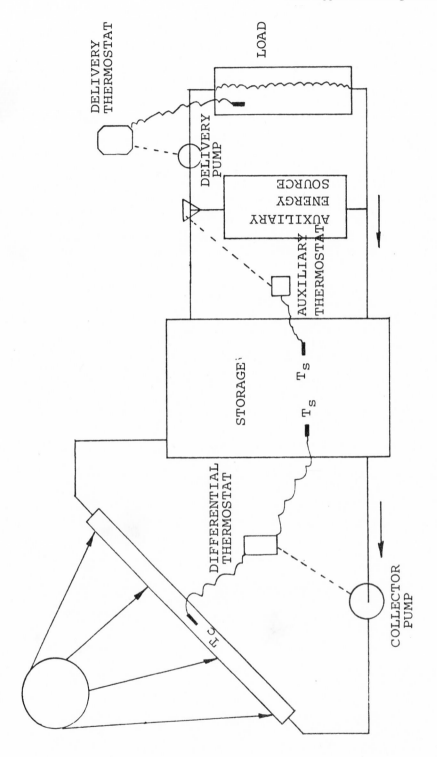

Figure III-29. *Typical controls for solar heat system with auxiliary energy source*

SOLAR TECHNOLOGY
References

1. "Solar Energy Utilization for Heating and Cooling," *ASHRAE Handbook and Product Directory, Applications,* Chap. 59, American Society of Heating, Refrigerating and Air-Conditioning Engineers, New York, 1974.
2. John A. Duffie and William A. Beckman, *Solar Energy Thermal Processes,* Wiley, New York, 1974.
3. D.K. Edwards, *Solar Collector Design,* The Franklin Institute Press, Philadelphia, 1977.
4. James E. Hill, Elmer R. Streed, George E. Kelly, Jon C. Geist, and Tamami Kusuda, *Development of Proposed Standards for Testing Solar Collectors and Thermal Storage Devices,* National Bureau of Standards Technical Note 899, U.S. Government Printing Office, Washington, D.C., 1976.
5. *Solar Heating Systems Design Manual,* International Telephone and Telegraph Corp., Morton Grove, Illinois, 1976.
6. Arthur R. Patton, *Solar Energy for Heating and Cooling of Buildings,* Noyes Data Corp., Park Ridge, New Jersey, 1975.
7. *Introduction to Solar Heating and Cooling Design and Sizing,* DOE/CS-0011, U.S. Dept. of Energy, Washington, D.C., 1978.
8. Harrison J. Killian, Gordon L. Dugger, and Jerry Grey, Eds., *Solar Energy for Earth,* American Institute of Aeronautics and Astronautics, New York, 1975.
9. C.A. Flood, Jr., J.L. Koon, and R.N. Brewer, "Solar Heating of Poultry Houses: 1. An Analysis of Energy Use for Brooding Broiler Chickens," *Poultry Sci.* **58(2),** 314 (1979).
10. *Solar Heating and Cooling of Buildings (Phase 0),* NSF-RANN Report NSF/RA/N-74-022B, TRW Systems Group, Redondo Beach, California, 1974.
11. T.H. Short, P.C. Badger, and W.L. Roller, "A Solar Pond for Heating Greenhouses and Rural Residences," *Proceedings Conference on Solar Energy for Heating Greenhouses and Greenhouse-Residence Combinations,* U.S. Dept. of Energy, Cleveland, Ohio, March 1977.
12. S.M. Ko and P.O. McCormick, "Desiccant as Drying Agent/Heat storage Media for Crop Drying by Solar Energy," *Proceedings Solar Crop Drying Conference,* North Carolina State University, Raleigh, June 1977.

IV. AGRICULTURAL USE

Livestock Structures

Confinement of livestock, particularly poultry and swine, requires a large amount of low-temperature heat to maintain a comfortable and healthful environment. For example, when poultry are very young, confinement temperatures must be kept as high as 22°C (72°F) or more to sustain life and promote the optimum combination of maximum growth and feed efficiency. However, during the growth period (4-8 weeks), higher temperatures reduce the growth rate (see Table IV-1[1]). As the animals grow, their bodies become more able to self heat so that lower environmental temperatures are tolerable. However, the energy demand remains high because the large volume of ventilation air used to remove moisture, toxic gases, dust, and odors from the house must be heated to room temperature. This adds as much as

Table IV-1. Effect of broiler-house rearing temperature on chicken weight and feed consumption per 1000 broilers for the 4- to 8-week growing period

House temperature °C	Chicken weight, live kg	Feed consumption kg	Chicken value @ 71¢/kg	Feed cost at $143 per metric ton	Chicken value minus feed cost
7	1614	4035	$1139	$578	$561
13	1602	3829	1130	549	581
18	1641	3709	1150	532	626
24	1570	3454	1108	495	613

70% to the heat demand of the building.[2] Solar energy can supply varying amounts of this heat, depending on the time of year and the ambient temperature.

Solar energy is also being used experimentally to supplement conventional sources in heating water for various phases of milk production and processing. In many dairies, water is heated to 70°C (158°F) or more and is used hot or mixed with cold water for use in the milking parlor[3] (see Figure IV-1). The hot water is necessary for proper cleaning and sanitation of all dairy equipment. An uninterrupted supply depends on the availability of fuel for the water heaters. As fuel availability becomes uncertain and cost rises, alternate energy sources must be found.

Poultry Houses

Space heating of poultry houses for brooding and growing young chickens, turkeys, and ducks is a primary area of agricultural energy consumption. The total

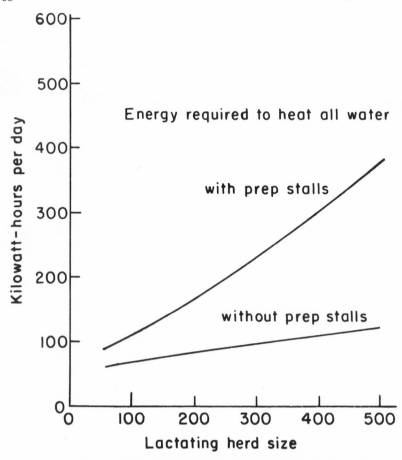

Figure IV-1. *Daily energy use in dairies for hot and warm water*

annual use of energy for brooding poultry in the United States has reached 1.95 x 10^{13} kJ (1.85 x 10^{13} Btu)[4], obtained mainly from liquefied petroleum gas (LPG), coal, fuel oil, and electricity, in descending order of importance (Table IV-2). A large portion of this energy is used in the southeastern United States, from eastern Texas through Arkansas to North Carolina, which produces about 75% of the broiler chickens.

Fuel requirements vary seasonally from about 75–115 liters (20–30 gallons) of LPG per 1000 chickens started in summer to over 375 liters (100 gallons) per 1000 started in midwinter. Most of this fuel is consumed during the brooding phase of the 8-week production cycle, about 30% in the first week, over 90% by the end of the third week. The fuel requirement has been reduced in recent years by success in improving house insulation, mechanical ventilation, and heating systems and by limited-area brooding.

Table IV-2. Volume of fuel used for brooding U.S. poultry, 1974

Kind of poultry	Region*	LPG liters	Natural gas megajoules	Oil liters	Coal metric tons
Broilers	1	215,529,261	579,934,952	9,836,015	83,865
	2	164,709,318	326,971,983	11,138,560	17,518
	3	4,476,855	**	15,088,603	**
	All regions	384,715,434	906,906,935	36,063,178	101,382
Layers	1	19,803,243	**	5,457,527	**
	2	42,615,555	286,919,631	**	**
	3	10,231,208	**	4,553,154	**
	All regions	72,650,006	286,919,631	10,010,681	**
Turkeys	1	29,892,955	160,995,215	**	**
	2	35,138,988	822,943	1,851,937	2,755
	3	36,491,625	161,332,622	**	**
	All regions	101,523,568	323,150,781	1,851,937	2,755
Ducks	All regions	1,325,409	441,683,791	449,820	**
Total		560,214,417	1,958,661,138	48,375,767	104,138
Percent of all poultry		81.2	3.2	7.6	8.0

*Local cold weather in degree days (°F): Region 1, 0–3000; Region 2, 3000–6500; Region 3, over 6500.

**None reported by growers and company managers interviewed.

Solar energy systems are being tested to replace fossil fuels as the primary heat source for poultry brooding. In one example, Reece and Deaton[1] combined liquid and air collectors to furnish 24-hour heat for brooding broilers (Figure IV-2). The water collection and storage system supplied nighttime heating, and ventilation air prewarmed by the air collectors filled much of the daytime requirements.

Collectors were flat-plate types, commercially available double-glazed PPG Baseline models for the water-heating system, and locally designed and built units (Figure IV-3) for air heating. A continuous ventilation system drawing air through the radiator (Figure IV-2) transferred all heat from the solar energy system (contributed by both collectors) to the chicken brooding and growing area. At midday, when the flow from the air-heating collector is warmer than the water in the radiator it passes through, some of the heat in the air is transferred to the water, adding to the energy storage. The warmed water in the radiator rises to the top and flows toward the storage tank, starting a clockwise thermosiphon circulation as viewed in Figure IV-2. At night, when the flow from the air-heating collector is cool, it draws heat from the water in the radiator which then circulates in the reverse direction.

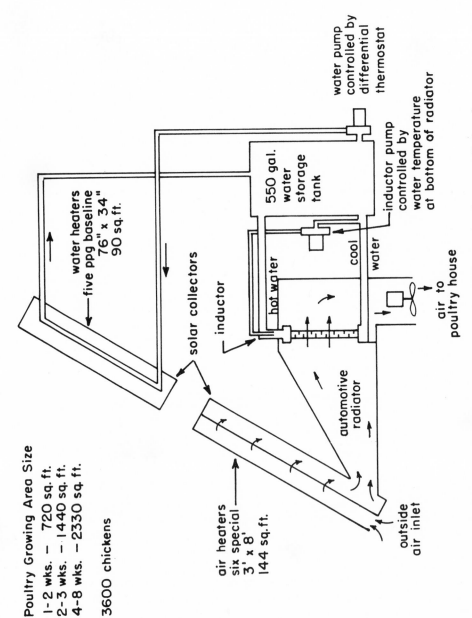

Poultry Growing Area Size

1-2 wks. —   720 sq. ft.
2-3 wks. — 1440 sq. ft.
4-8 wks. — 2330 sq. ft.

3600 chickens

water heaters
five ppg baseline
76" x 34"
90 sq. ft.

solar collectors

inductor

hot water

cool

water

550 gal.
water
storage
tank

water pump
controlled by
differential
thermostat

inductor pump
controlled by
water temperature
at bottom of radiator

air to
poultry house

automotive
radiator

air heaters
six special
3' x 8'
144 sq. ft.

outside
air inlet

Figure IV-2. *Solar collector/storage system for heating poultry-house ventilation air*

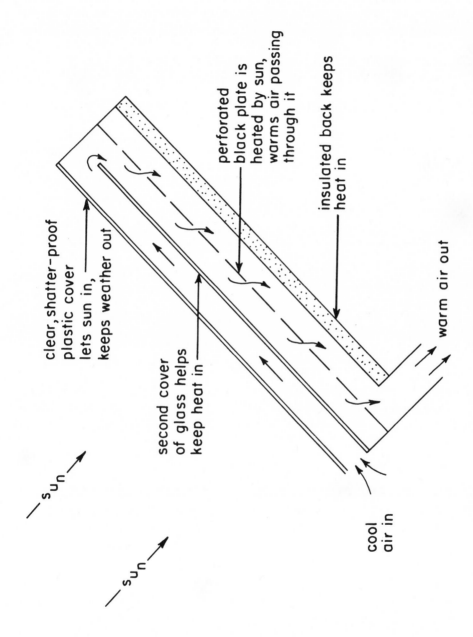

clear, shatter-proof
plastic cover
lets sun in,
keeps weather out

second cover
of glass helps
keep heat in

perforated
black plate is
heated by sun,
warms air passing
through it

insulated back keeps
heat in

sun

sun

cool
air in

warm air out

Figure IV-3. *Design and operation of solar panels used to heat ventilation air for broiler research house.*

Table IV-3 shows the system's efficiency for the winter of 1974-1975 when fuel consumption was 73% less than in 1975-1976 when all heat came from LPG. For a similar brood grown during 8 weeks of the winter of 1977 with an average outside

Table IV-3. Weekly LPG fuel consumption per 1000 chickens for winter broiler brooding and growing in Mississippi: 1974-5 — LPG only, 1975-6 — with solar heating

| | House | Without solar | | With solar | |
| | temperature | LPG | Outside temperature | LPG | Outside temperature |
Week	°C	liters	°C	liters	°C
1	29.4	27.3	7.8	4.9	10.6
2	26.7	34.8	6.7	7.9	11.7
3	23.9	22.0	10.0	9.1	1.1
4	21.1	9.5	15.6	9.1	6.1
5	21.1	13.6	5.0	*	3.9
6	21.1	8.3	13.3		2.8
7	21.1	*	11.1		3.3
8	21.1		10.6		8.9
		Total 115.5	Ave. 10.6	Total 31.0	Ave. 6.1

*Brooder stoves and pilot lights turned off.

temperature of 5°C (41°F), the solar system supplied 75% of all heat (Table IV-4). This combination of solar system design and poultry house management saved significant quantities of fuel without reducing bird quality or production.

Table IV-4. Energy consumption in LPG equivalent liters/1000 birds for broiler chicken test, January 11–February 28, 1977

| | Type of heat | | Temperature | | |
| | Solar | Electric | Outside | Inside | Ventilation/bird |
Week	liter (equiv.)	liter (equiv.)	°C	°C	m³/min
1	11.4	19.3	−0.6	27.9	.0017
2	12.1	11.4	−0.4	27.1	.0031
3	15.9	4.2	2.0	24.8	.0062
4	18.2	–	3.5	22.7	.0113
5	14.4	–	9.2	22.7	.0212
6	18.9	–	7.1	22.6	.0252
7	11.1	–	13.2	23.7	.0532
Total	102.0	34.9			

Litter moisture content at end of test: 25% w.b.

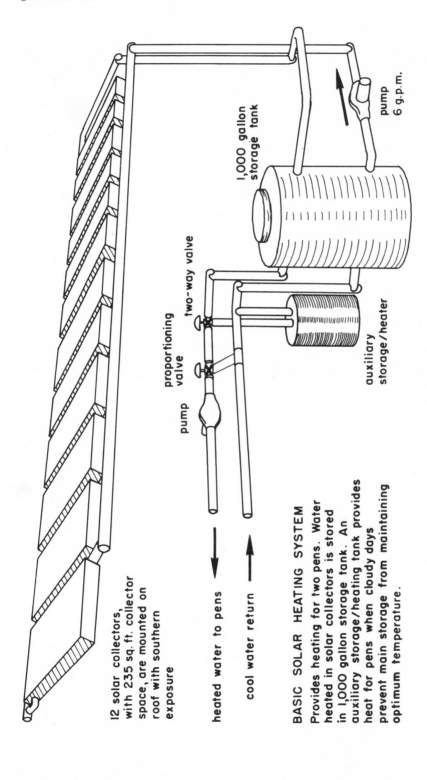

12 solar collectors, with 235 sq. ft. collector space, are mounted on roof with southern exposure

1,000 gallon storage tank

pump 6 g.p.m.

two-way valve

proportioning valve

pump

auxiliary storage/heater

heated water to pens

cool water return

BASIC SOLAR HEATING SYSTEM

Provides heating for two pens. Water heated in solar collectors is stored in 1,000 gallon storage tank. An auxiliary storage/heating tank provides heat for pens when cloudy days prevent main storage from maintaining optimum temperature.

Figure IV-4. One section of the Auburn solar-heated water system for broiler brooding and growing

Brewer and Flood[5] have also used solar-heated water as a main energy source for brooding and growing broilers. Their system consisted of three sections like the one shown schematically in Figure IV-4, with double-glazed flat-plate collectors mounted on the poultry house roof giving a total collection area of approximately 65 square meters (700 square feet), and 11,350 liters (3000 gallons) of water for heat storage. It had no heat exchangers and the same water flowed through the collector, storage, and delivery circuits. No antifreeze was necessary because the water drained down into storage when solar radiation was not available. A differential thermostat started each collector pump when the collector water temperature was 15°C (27°F) above that in its storage tank, and stopped it when the temperature difference reached 1.7°C (3°F). Two-position, three-way, pneumatically activated bronze valves switched from the solar energy system to auxiliary commercial electric water heaters when the storage temperatures dropped below a preset level.

Two systems of heat delivery were evaluated. One consisted of exposed 2.54-cm (1-inch) diameter finned tubes along one wall of the brooding chamber, and the other used an array of equally spaced water pipes encased in concrete slabs which occupied approximately half the brooding chamber. Modifications were also tested in attempts to improve efficiency of heat delivery. In brooding trials to 6 weeks of age during all seasons, solar energy supplied 24–100% of the energy requirements. Table IV-5 gives average results. Long periods of cloudy weather during the broods started in November and January reduced the solar contribution. This is to be expected and must be considered in solar system design.[6]

Commercial poultry farmers have exploited solar energy by various means, primarily passive, to reduce fuel requirements. For example, the design of a poultry house or other livestock structure must take into account the sun's effect on building temperature during both hot and cold seasons. Ventilation and management considerations dictate that poultry houses should be no wider than 12–13 meters (40–42

Table IV-5. Percent auxiliary energy required to supplement solar water heating in poultry brooding tests, summary of 5 trials, Alabama 1977-8

| | Heating method | |
| | Finned tube % | Concrete slab % |
Time of year		
Summer — fall	0	0
November start	74	59
January start	48.6	48.3
Late winter — early spring	17.1	9.8
Late spring — early summer	0	0

feet). Length presents no major problems. The roof, normally insulated and made of reflecting material, is designed to be the main barrier to the sun's heat. Orienting the building's long axis approximately east-west, and providing the correct roof overhang on the south wall relative to the wall height, shield the wall from direct sunlight during hot months and allow the sun to warm the wall during cold months. This does much to balance the overall yearly energy load.

Some mechanical ventilation systems take advantage of the sun-warmed south wall by taking in air on that side and exhausting it at the north wall. On a sunny day during cold weather, this feature can significantly raise the inlet air temperature.

To date, commercial efforts to trap the sun's energy have favored less expensive means which also tend to be less efficient. One common method uses rock beds covered by glass or plastic glazing, as in Figure IV-5, to heat ventilation air. Another method receiving some attention uses the roof as an air heater by covering it with fiberglass sheathing that readily admits the sun's rays (Figure IV-6). The roof collector may be used with or without storage capabilities.

Carefully planned integration of energy conservation and solar energy systems can significantly reduce the poultry industry's dependence on fossil fuels and ensure

Figure IV-5. *Glazing over rock bed in a Georgia commercial poultry house*

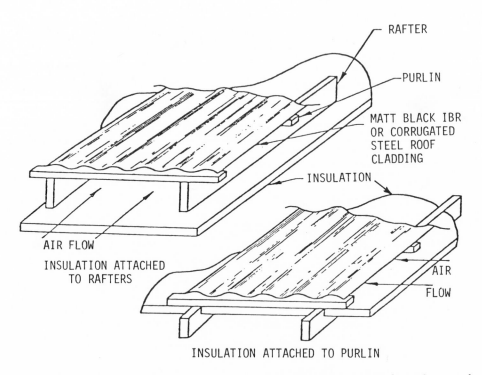

RAFTER

PURLIN

MATT BLACK IBR
OR CORRUGATED
STEEL ROOF
CLADDING

INSULATION

INSULATION

AIR FLOW

INSULATION ATTACHED
TO RAFTERS

AIR
FLOW

INSULATION ATTACHED TO PURLIN

Figure IV-6. *Solar air heaters sheathed with transparent fiberglass on south-facing barn roof*

a continued abundance of poultry meat and eggs. The major questions to be answered concern economic feasibility and operating reliability. More complete application of solar energy systems would reduce unit costs and help to make the systems economically feasible. For example, multi-stage brooding would allow a solar system to serve more than one poultry house.[7] The system would supply brood house No. 1 for 3 weeks, providing 80-90% of the total required energy during this period, then switch to brood house No. 2, and so on. If managerial and disease-control problems can also be solved, this system could pay for itself in about 14 years. More innovative housing and management methods are needed.

Swine

The commercial hog industry uses a large amount of low-temperature energy for brooding baby pigs and for warming nursery and finishing units, particularly in colder areas of the United States. Meador et al[8] found the ideal environmental temperature for newborn pigs to be about 32°C (89°F) initially, falling gradually to 21°C (70°F) in about 10 days. Other researchers have recommended early temperatures as high as 36°C (97°F), depending on whether bedding is used. The sow is more comfortable at about 15°C (59°F) and becomes restless when temperatures are too high. The sources of heat are mainly liquified petroleum gas (LPG) and electricity (Table IV-6).

Table IV-6. Energy consumption and sources for swine production, 1974 data base

Operation	Total energy 10⁹ kilojoule	Gasoline		Diesel fuel		LPG		Electricity	
		kiloliter	% of total energy	kiloliter	% of total energy	kiloliter	% of total energy	10⁶ kwhr	% of total energy
Lighting	348	—	—	—	—	—	—	97	100
Feed handling	5363	20025	13	110727	81	—	—	96	6
Waste disposal	3730	14760	14	82109	86	—	—	3	1
Water supply	2869	—	—	—	—	—	—	797	96
Assembly-handling	24	693	100	—	—	—	—	—	—
Space heating	5500	—	—	4	1	189982	89	130	9
Ventilation	3070	—	—	—	—	—	—	852	100
Water heating	50	—	—	—	—	—	—	13	96
Other farm vehicles	11480	216892	66	100567	34	—	—	—	—
Farm auto	6336	181855	100	—	—	—	—	—	—
Others	428	1378	11	8581	78	—	—	13	11
Total	39198	435603	39	301988	30	189982	12	2001	19

Preliminary data developed by the Economic Research Service, USDA, Washington, D.C. under a jointly funded cooperative agreement with the Federal Energy Administration. Data include all energy used directly on the farm for crop and livestock production (small discrepancies in addition may appear due to rounding of numbers). Invested energy includes the energy required to manufacture fertilizers and pesticides (including carrier solutions).

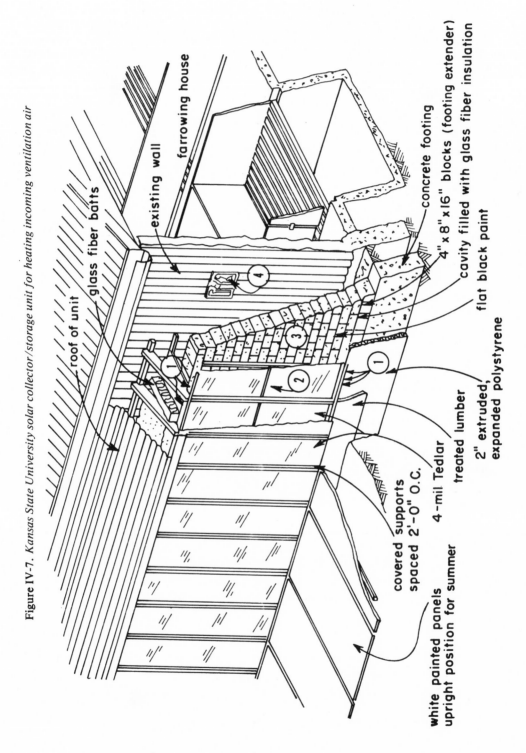

Figure IV-7. *Kansas State University solar collector/storage unit for heating incoming ventilation air*

Heat is brought to the pigs and the sow in various ways. In one method, the building air is heated to an intermediate level and spot heat is added as needed. Perhaps the most practical means is to heat the concrete slab under the young pigs but not in the area occupied by the sow. Heat is supplied by electric heating cables or hot-water pipes embedded in the concrete. The latter method lends itself readily to the use of solar-heated water.

The solar system can be the primary heat source or a supplement to another system. For example, a solar unit at Kansas State University (Spillman et al[9]) is designed to heat incoming ventilation air simply and economically, augmenting but not replacing the conventional heating system. Figure IV-7 shows the construction of the collector-storage unit.

A south-facing wall painted with flat-black Rustoleum is constructed of solid concrete blocks stacked but not mortared so that ventilation air can flow through the cracks. The wall is both collector and storage medium and can also bear weight. A transparent, double-glazed collector cover consists of 4-mil plastic films 3.8 cm (1.5 inch) apart in a wood frame which holds the inner film 3.8 cm away from the black concrete surface. Tedlar film is being used, but various cover materials have been evaluated. The choice depends on considerations of cost, lifetime, and solar transmittance.

Air enters at the top and bottom (arrows labeled 1 in Figure IV-7), flows between the glazings, through an open slot (2) in the inner film, and against the black face (3) of the concrete wall. Now heated, it passes through the cracks between the blocks, into the plenum behind the collector wall, and through the fan (4) to the building interior where it is used.

Although the system's effectiveness varies with climatic conditions, insolation level, and air temperatures to be maintained, projected LPG fuel savings of 7.5 liter per square foot of collector area proved to be realistic.[9] Systems similar in design and operation to the Kansas State research unit were installed on a commercial hog farm and tested for 2 years.

Two solar-heated, 32-sow farrowing houses were constructed on the producer's farm during the fall and winter of 1976-1977. The buildings are 8.5 x 29 meters (28 x 96 feet) and each is equipped with a 2.3 x 29-meter (7.5 x 96-foot) solar collector-storage wall. Installed (1976) cost was approximately $23/m^2 ($7/ft^2), amounting to $140 per farrowing crate.[2] On the same site, two 8 x 29-meter (26 x 96-foot) 32-sow farrowing houses, about 8 years old, were available for comparison of energy use. Propane and electric metering systems allowed separate measurement of the conventional energy consumed in each house. Each house had about 4 farrowing cycles during the test period, but number and weight of animals were not always the same.

Although buildings differed somewhat in heat loss and heating method, the solar-heated buildings realized significant energy and cost savings (Table IV-7 and IV-8).

Table IV-7. Propane and electrical energy used in the buildings at
Producer A's farm, Sept. 20, 1977 to July 6, 1978

Building	Propane liters	Electricity kwhr
EB3 (conventional)	14517	5197
EB4 (conventional)	17196	4172
SB5 (solar)	6552	8660
SB6 (solar)	5137	6341

Table IV-8. Cost of energy used in the buildings at Producer A's farm, Sept. 20, 1977
to July 6, 1978

Building	Propane @$0.37/gal ($0.098/liter)	Electricity @$0.03/kwhr	Total
EB3 (conventional)	$1417	$156	$1573
EB4 (conventional)	1679	125	1804
SB5 (solar)	640	260	900
SB6 (solar)	502	190	692

Ofthe $883 maximum difference between a conventional (EB3) and a solar (SB6)
building, $560 was estimated to be attributable to the solar collector-storage unit.
(See Section V, *Economic Implications,* for a more detailed discussion of costs and
savings.)

Initial cost of a solar system relative to the energy requirements is a major design
consideration. For example, the system in Figure IV-8[8], which uses a free-standing
collector and hot-water storage for farrowing-pad heating cost approximately $625
per farrowing crate. Performance data are not available to compare this system with
the one described above, but it is obvious that the energy savings must be considerably greater to justify the greater initial expenditure.

Dairies

Commercial dairies require large amounts of energy to heat water for cleaning
equipment and for stimulation and cleaning of udders. As in the case of farrowing

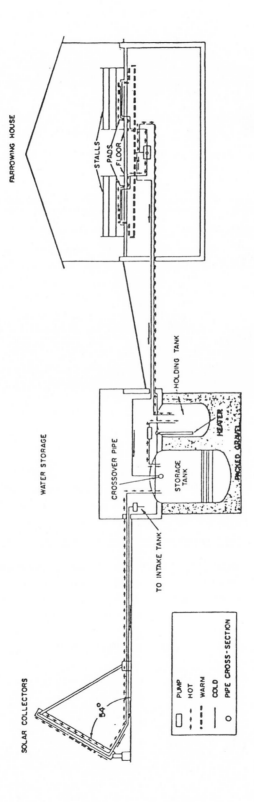

Figure IV-8. *Free-standing solar collector and liquid-storage system for heating farrowing pad*

Table IV-9. Energy sources and consumption for milk-cow production, 1974 data base

Operation	Total energy 10^9 kilojoule	Gasoline kiloliter	% of total energy	LPG kiloliter	% of total energy	Electricity 10^6 kwhr	% of total energy
Lighting	1461	—		—		406	100
Feed handling	6805	163287	84	—		310	16
Waste disposal	9841	270070	96	—		120	4
Water supply	1258	—		—		349	100
Space heating	573	—		21838	100	—	
Ventilation	2205	—		—		612	100
Water heating	10551	—		267769	65	961	33
Milking	2954	—		—		820	100
Milk cooling	4840	—		—		1344	100
Farm auto	9.5	257	100	—		—	
Other	14339	392808	95	—		182	5
Total	54843	826423	53	289606	13	5105	34

Preliminary data developed by the Economic Research Service, USDA, Washington, D.C. under a jointly funded cooperative agreement with the Federal Energy Administration. Data include all energy used directly on the
farm for crop and livestock production (small discrepancies in addition may appear due to rounding of
numbers). Invested energy includes the energy required to manufacture fertilizers and pesticides (including carrier solutions).

houses, much of this energy is conventionally supplied by LPG and electricity (Table
IV-9). About half could potentially be drawn from relatively low-temperature alternative sources such as solar flat-plate collectors. Effective conservation methods
within the dairy to reduce routine usage of hot or warm water could effect additional
savings.

For example, a study of over 100 dairies throughout the United States[3] revealed
wide variations in hot water consumption. Figure IV-9 shows average daily use for
udder wash and stimulation. Observers found that a well run dairy used one-third to
one-half less hot water than the average. Reducing over-use of hot water may be a
key factor in making solar energy practical for a commercial dairy.

Use of hot, 75°C (160°F), and warm, 49°C (105°F), water varies with the size and
physical and mechanical arrangement of the dairy. Warm water consumption per
cow, without automatic prep stalls, ranges from about 5.7 liter (1½ gallon) for small
dairies to about 3.8 liter (1 gallon) for large ones. As indicated in Figure IV-9,
automatic prep stalls raise warm water consumption to about 19–22 liter (5–6
gallons). Increased use of warm water greatly increases the energy load and must be
modified as energy becomes more costly and less available.

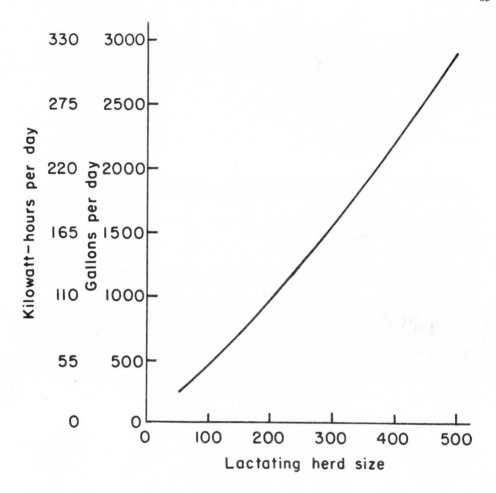

Figure IV-9. *Daily consumption of energy and warm water for udder washing and stimulation in dairies with automatic prep stalls*

Researchers at the USDA Agricultural Research Center in Beltsville, Maryland, heat water and living space for a 200-cow herd with a solar system having a 93-m² (1000-ft²) flat-plate collector and 15,140-liter (4000-gallon) storage.[10] Figure IV-10 gives an exterior view of the system showing the roof-mounted, south-facing collectors and partially buried fiberglass storage tank. Figure IV-11 is a diagram of water flow. Cool water is pumped from the bottom of the storage tank (return from the heat load) to the collector bank. Solar-heated water returns to the top of the tank (supply to heat load). To avoid the freezing problems frequently encountered with some collectors, the USDA unit has a pump-assisted drain-down system which automatically drains all water from the collectors when the solar pumps turn off.

Figure IV-10. *Solar research dairy, U.S. Department of Agriculture, Beltsville, Maryland*

Heat for hot water has been supplied by three sources: electric water heaters, a supplemental waste-heat plant, and the solar energy system. Figure IV-12 shows the energy drawn from each source from January to June, 1978.[11] The solar contribution ranged from 16% in January to 59% in June and averaged 35%.

These findings are encouraging and indicate the practicality of the application. However, a solar water-heating system capable of supplying all hot water requirements would be prohibitively expensive. It is more practical to obtain as much hot water from the solar system as is economically reasonable and to depend on conventional energy sources for auxiliary heat.

Summary

Heating water and/or air for poultry brooding and growing, swine farrowing and intermediate growing, and clean-up and space heating in commercial dairies were shown to be technically sound and economically feasible applications of solar energy. Solar systems supplied some 75% of broiler-brooding heat requirements on a Mississippi farm, 24-100% in Alabama. A Kansas system in one year saved $560 in fuel costs on a 32-sow commercial swine unit. Solar heat met an average of 35% of

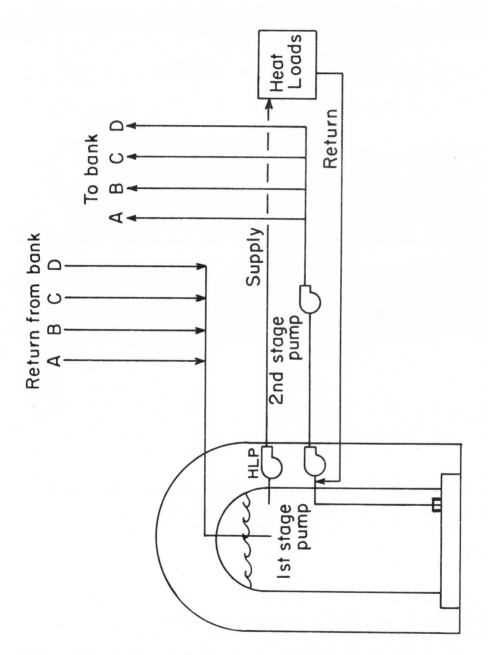

Figure IV-11. *Water flow to and from collector bank, storage, and heat load in solar research dairy unit, U.S. Department of Agriculture, Beltsville, Maryland*

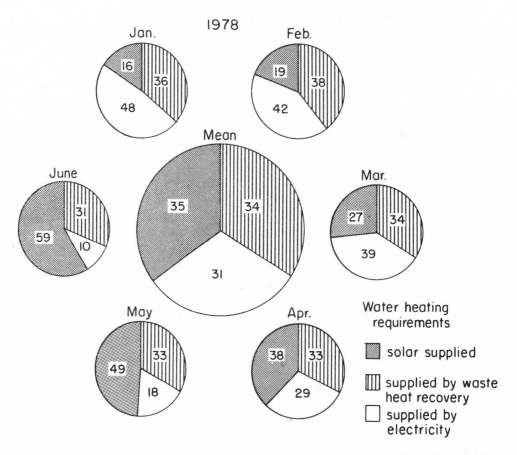

Figure IV-12. *Contributions from various energy sources to water heating for solar research dairy requirements, U.S. Department of Agriculture, Beltsville, Maryland*

the total requirements of a 200-cow dairy in Maryland. Testing continues, but it is already apparent that solar energy can lessen the dependence on conventional fuel and reduce costs with an appropriate choice of application and system design.

Prospects for the Future

Although the above discussion touched only on poultry, swine, and dairy production, other livestock structures also present opportunities for application of solar energy. Generally, any closed or semi-closed environment building requiring heat for livestock or other animals is a possible candidate.

Unfortunately, many buildings now housing animals were not constructed with efficient energy use and conservation in mind. Retrofit of these structures for economical solar heating may be difficult and costly in most cases and impossible in some. However, as new technology and management procedures help to solve some of the problems, more effort must be directed to efficient energy use in existing buildings because they may still have 20–50 years of useful life left.

The design of new livestock structures should take full advantage of methods for controlling the effect of solar radiation on building interiors. Appropriate orientation, construction, insulation, and ventilation can dramatically influence energy requirements. Passive exploitation of the sun's energy can be a major contributing factor to the accelerated introduction of active solar heating systems.

LIVESTOCK STRUCTURES
References

1. F.N. Reece and J.W. Deaton, "Solar Heat Cuts Broiler House Fuel Cost almost 75 per cent," *Broiler Business,* April 1976.
2. C.K. Spillman, F.V. Robbins, and R.H. Hines, "Solar Energy for Reducing Fossil Fuel Usage in Farrowing Houses," *Proceedings Symposium on Solar Energy for Livestock Production,* University of Maryland, College Park, 1978.
3. F. Wiersma and D.L. Larson, "Solar and Heat Recovery Systems to Heat Water for Dairies," *ibid.*
4. R.N. Brewer and J.R. Dunn, *Potential for Conversion and Utilization of Solar Energy in Poultry Production,* Final Report NSF/RANN/SE/PTP74-23987/PR/74/4, National Science Foundation, Washington, D.C., 1975.
5. R.N. Brewer and C.A. Flood, *Solar Heated Poultry House,* Auburn University Agricultural Experiment Station Leaflet 96, Auburn, Alabama, July 1978.
6. Roger R. Getz and Michael M. Nicholas, *Probabilities and Extremes of Solar Radiation by Climatic Week,* National Weather Service Technical Memorandum SR-98, National Oceanic and Atmospheric Administration, Washington, D.C., 1979.
7. Morris White, "An Economic Appraisal of Use of Solar Energy in Broiler Production," *Proceedings Symposium on Use of Solar Energy for Poultry and Livestock Production,* Auburn, Alabama, November 1976.
8. N.F. Meador, L. Eggerman, and K.L. McFate, "Solar Heating of Water for Baby Pig Environmental Control," *loc cit* in reference 2.
9. C.K. Spillman, F.V. Robbins, and B.A. Koch, "Solar Energy for Preheating Ventilating Air (Swine Buildings)," *loc cit* in reference 7, pp. 140-151.
10. M.B. Hayden, "Solar Energy for Milking Parlor Heating and Cooling," *loc cit* in reference 2.
11. P. Thompson and M.G. Clary, *Solar Heating for Milking Parlors,* Farmers Bulletin No. 2266, U.S. Dept. of Agriculture, Agricultural Research Service, Washington, D.C., 1977.

Greenhouses and Greenhouse-Residences

Greenhouses are designed to produce a profitable crop under controlled conditions. With proper management, greenhouse yields can be 5 to 15 times those expected in the open field and can be maintained over an extended growing season. The main requirements are sufficient sunlight, or an artificial substitute, and auxiliary energy for heat and ventilation. Historically, fossil fuels have supplied the auxiliary heat, and electricity has supplied the ventilation and artificial light.

The transparent glass, polyethylene, or acrylic walls and roofs of a typical greenhouse make heat management difficult. Heat easily passes in and out. During daylight hours, as much as 85% of the sun's rays may enter and be trapped as heat by absorpiion and reradiation at longer wavelengths (the greenhouse effect). Even on cold days, ventilation may be needed to remove excess heat so that the temperature remains controlled. However, when solar radiation is not available, at night or on cloudy days, auxiliary heat is necessary to maintain desired temperatures. Heat losses are variable, increasing with faster air movement over the greenhouse surface, greater ventilation, rain, and construction faults.

One of the first steps in designing an energy management system for a greenhouse is calculation of heat transfer dynamics. The equation for heat loss by conduction is:

$$Q_c = AU\Delta T$$

where Q_c is the rate of heat conduction, watt

A is the exposed surface area of the barrier material, m^2

U is the heat flow factor (a combination of thermal conductivity and material thickness), watt/m^2-°C

ΔT is the temperature difference between inside and outside surfaces, °C

The equation for infiltration losses is:

$$Q_A = 0.37\, VN\Delta T$$

where Q_A is the heat lost by air exchange, watt

V is the greenhouse volume, m^3

N is the number of complete air changes per hour

Table IV-10. Transmission of solar radiation through various greenhouse cover materials, high noon near Denver, Colorado, November 1977 to March 1978[2]

Structure	Details	Transmission %
Quonset	No condensate	59.2
	Condensate	54.3
Peaked	Standard fiber-reinforced plastic (FRP) with polyethylene liner	34.4
	FRP + Tedlar	51.6
	FRP + new Tedlar and polyethylene liner	45.8
	Glass, north-south orientation (November)	79.3
	Glass, east-west orientation (March)	94.0

Since greenhouses use solar radiation through the glazing for both heating and catalyzing plant growth,[1] attempts to reduce heat loss must not deprive plants of essential sunlight. For example, winter sunshine in northern latitudes may be inadequate to support proper plant growth, requiring supplemental artificial light. If extra glazing or greenhouse covers are used to reduce heat loss, they will also restrict the transmission of sunlight and increase the need for artificial light. The extra energy for lighting may cost more than the heat energy saved. Table IV-10 shows transmission characteristics of various greenhouse cover materials.[2]

Heat conservation methods vary with greenhouse type but have a common goal: to control heat loss without adversely affecting light intensity and production systems. Measures tried with varying success include double glazing with glass or other materials, removable blankets, draw drapes, or insulation boards, and foaming the top of the greenhouse at night and removing the foam during the day. Table IV-11 shows the effectiveness of some of these methods. Since considerable heat loss is expected, and fossil fuel usage is high, some method of storing excess solar energy for nighttime use is desirable.

Solar energy may be used passively in small hobby greenhouses to furnish most of the heat necessary to grow cold-tolerant plants. The best example of this is the pit-type greenhouse (Figure IV-13), built free standing or attached to another building. A portion of the greenhouse lies about 1.2 m (4 ft) below ground level where the surrounding earth is self-insulated from the surface and usually keeps the greenhouse above freezing temperature. Other passive methods include such features as crushed-rock floors painted black or an insulated black-painted north wall (sunlight passes through the transparent south wall to strike the north wall) to absorb and

Table IV-11. Effect of heat-conservation measures on annual fuel-oil consumption of a 1300-m² (14,000-ft²) glass greenhouse in central Pennsylvania

| | Fuel use | |
	liters	% of average demand
Base only (lapped glass, gable shape)	114,868	100
Base + single film plastic on all walls	102,206	89
Base + single film plastic on south wall, R-8 insulation on north wall	97,626	85
Base + single film plastic on walls and interior thin blankets	63,973	56
Base + interior thin blankets	76,957	67
Base + double-inflated plastic film over entire surface	60,869	53
Base + double-inflated plastic film over entire surface and interior thin blankets	41,337	36

store heat during the day. Hobby greenhouses have the advantage of being used only during mild weather as the owner wishes.

Figure IV-13. *Pit greenhouse — heat stored in soil keeps greenhouse temperature above freezing*

A parabolic aquaculture-greenhouse at Pragtree Farm, Arlington, Washington, is a prototype of a passively heated greenhouse (Figure IV-14).[3] It is 4.0 m (13 ft) wide by 9.8 m (32 ft) long, 4.0 m tall at its highest point, and incorporates a 29.7-m² (320-ft²) growing area and an 18,170-liter (4800-gallon) thermal storage pond with a 17.3-m² (186-ft²) top surface. The south face is single-glazed with lapped 406 x 457-

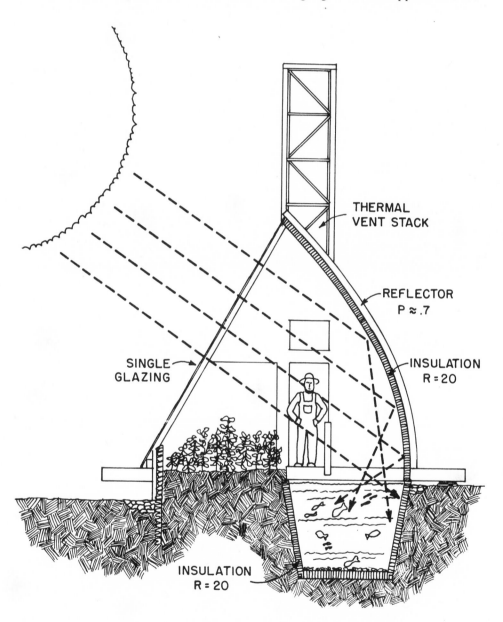

Figure IV-14. *Parabolic greenhouse with aquaculture pool*

mm (16 x 18-inch) standard greenhouse glass and tilted at a 60° angle above the horizontal. The north wall has a parabolic cross section, is insulated with SM™ styrofoam to a value (reciprocal of heat flow factor) of 2.6m²-°C/watt (15 ft²-°F/Btu per hr), and is covered with aluminized mylar reflective film with an assumed reflectivity of 0.7. East and west walls are partially glazed; the thermal vent stack rises 3.7 m (12 ft) above the top vent and is glazed on its south side.

The north wall acts as a parabolic mirror that reflects and concentrates radiation into the storage pond. Losses in this process serve to heat the greenhouse during the daytime. Calculated natural heat transfer from the storage pond to the greenhouse

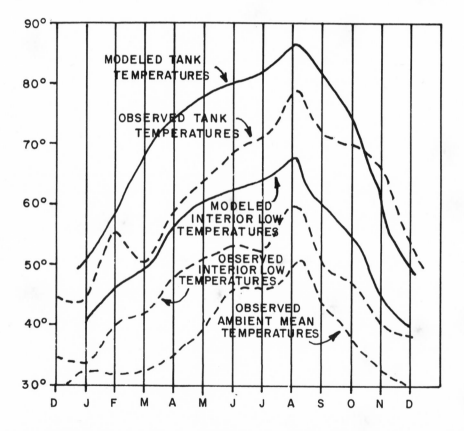

Figure IV-15. *Predicted and observed temperatures in parabolic greenhouse with aquaculture pool*

interior is approximately 333 watt/°C (630 Btu/hr-°F). Figure IV-15 shows the low interior temperatures calculated on the basis of a mathematical model and those actually observed.

Plant growth in the parabolic greenhouse was significantly better than in a single-glazed pit greenhouse, 4.3 x 12.2 m (14 x 40 ft) with twenty 208-liter (55-gal) drums for storage. The parabolic system may be well suited for certain species of fish that require warm water. However, more experience is needed before it can be used commercially.

Commercial greenhouses may be restricted to off-season production of food or potting plants to take advantage of higher prices. Solar systems for these greenhouses require separate collectors and storage to maximize solar energy utilization. Collectors may be standard free-standing units with air or liquid as a heat-transfer medium, feeding a liquid or rock storage designed as part of the greenhouse or housed separately. The heat exchange from solar storage must be integrated into the greenhouse environmental control system and usually requires an alternate energy source for times when solar energy is inadequate.

The design and size of solar system components must be consistent with the heat demand. Table IV-12 shows the total heat demand of a 1394-m² (15,000-ft²) greenhouse and the energy actually supplied by a modular collector-storage system.[1]

Table IV-12. Total heat demand of a 1394-m²(15,000-ft²) greenhouse and amount supplied by a modular solar collection-storage system[1]

Month	Heat, 10^8 kilojoule	
	Total	Solar
Jan	6.74	0.96
Feb	5.78	0.07
Mar	5.69	1.32
Apr	3.76	1.16
May	2.28	1.16
Jun	1.31	1.18
Jul	0.46	1.33
Aug	0.09	1.47
Sep	0.01	1.46
Oct	1.42	1.37
Nov	3.48	0.93
Dec	6.08	0.89
Total	37.1	13.3

The solar-heated module consists of a free-standing structure with the shape of a right triangular prism (right-angle wedge) having a 45.8 x 6.1-m (150 x 20-ft) base and a 6.1-m height. The sloped, south-facing wall is tilted to an angle of 55° from the horizontal and has a 465-m² (5000-ft²) glazed surface area. Inside the module is an insulated 37,850-liter (10,000-gallon) storage tank. One set of fancoil units transfers heat from the collector to storage, and another set, controlled by a mixing valve, disseminates heat within the greenhouse.

Table IV-13 shows an economic analysis of the heating module performed to estimate savings over a 20-year period for various initial costs and assumed fuel-

Table IV-13. Payback time in years vs solar-system construction costs for various rates of fuel-price increase

Excess of fuel-price increase over general inflation rate %	Construction cost per unit active collector surface		
	$270/m²	$215/m²	$161/m²
0	24	19	14
1	20	16	12
2	16	13	10
3	14	11	8
4	11	9	7

price increases. Actual system cost was approximately $270/m² ($25/ft²). Payback time depends on what happens to fuel prices and inflation rates, but this standard collector-storage-delivery system has a promising 11-year prospect if fuel prices rise at a rate 4% above that of general inflation. At that time, the solar module will have reached the break-even point and thereafter will register a net gain over a competing conventional fuel system.

The saline collector-storage pond, described in section III and illustrated in Figure III-22, is an attractive means for accumulating and storing excess heat all year for use only in winter because of its relatively low heat loss. Following a technique developed by Nielson[4], the Ohio Agricultural Research and Development Center, Wooster, Ohio, constructed a solar pond 8.5 m (28 ft) wide, 18.3 m (60 ft) long, and 3.7 m (12 ft) deep.[5] The lower half of the pond had a 20% salt concentration which gradually decreased from mid-depth upward, reaching 0% at the surface. The pond was covered with a greenhouse to reduce air currents at the water's surface, and reflectors were placed in the greenhouse to direct more heat into the pond. However, problems with diffusion of light by the greenhouse cover tended to decrease the effectiveness of the reflectors.

Heat was removed from the water by various methods. One was to pump pond brine through the outer shell of a coaxial tube heat exchanger. The brine gave up heat to fresh water in the central tube which transferred the heat to either a unit heat exchanger in the greenhouse, when the pond temperature was between 40 and 80°C (104 and 176°F), or to a heat pump when the pond temperature was between 5 and 40°C (41 and 176°F). During tests, brine was successfully pumped from the lower half of the pond and returned without disturbing the saline concentration gradient in the upper half of the pond. Although potentially valuable as a year-round solar collector-storage system, the solar pond requires further study before it can be put into general practice.

Solar-heated greenhouses may be especially suited for multiple-purpose use. North Carolina State University now operates a combination greenhouse-tobacco curing system at Raleigh, North Carolina.[6] This consists of a bulk-curing module inside a specially designed greenhouse and captures and stores solar energy in two ways. First, as a bulk-curing structure, it is equipped to directly collect, store, and use the sun's energy to cure tobacco. Second, as a greenhouse with part of the curing equipment removed, it uses solar energy for heating and photosynthesis.

Figure IV-16 shows a cross-sectional view. Solar radiation transmitted through the fiberglass cover is absorbed by the black surfaces of the absorbers. Air passing over the absorbers picks up heat and is used immediately to cure tobacco or transfers its heat to the gravel beds. At night and during the tobacco yellowing phase, the entire structure is used as a heat exchanger to condense out moisture. During leaf and stem drying, fresh air is drawn at night from the side air vents of the greenhouse through the gravel bed where it is preheated before entering the furnace.

Night operation saves some fuel, but maximum savings occur during daylight hours. In early tests, the overall fuel saving was 37% compared to a conventional bulk-curing barn used as a control (Table IV-14).[7] Tobacco quality was equal. Advanced collector and storage designs can be expected to increase the energy saving.

A solar heating system for a combined greenhouse-residence can perform more effectively than a similar system for a greenhouse or residence alone.[8] One factor that makes the combination compatible is that greater temperature variations are tolerable in a greenhouse than in a dwelling. For example, some plants may benefit from a diurnal temperature cycle of warm days and cool nights. Indications are that proper design and construction can significantly lower heating and cooling costs for both the greenhouse and the residence.

A solar system designed primarily for a greenhouse (or for grain drying, heating a livestock structure, or other agricultural operation) can sometimes be more fully utilized as a heat source for an existing residence as well. According to the 1970 census[9], the United States had some 16 million occupied rural homes, including both agricultural and non-agricultural dwellings. They varied in type but were generally poorly insulated. For all homes in the United States, the total annual energy from all

Figure IV-16. *Bulk tobacco curing in multiple-purpose greenhouse — direct solar heating by day, release of gravel-stored heat by night*

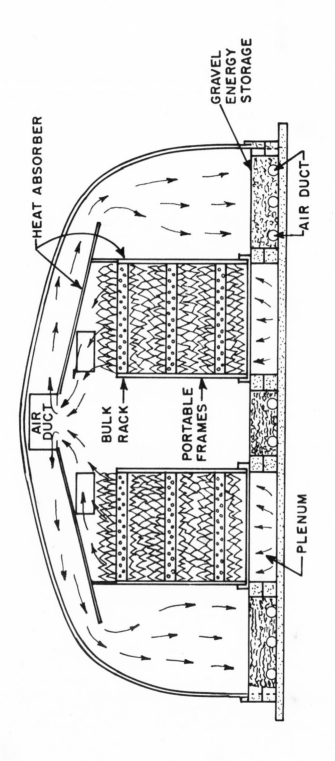

Table IV-14. Tobacco bulk curing: greenhouse vs conventional barn

Greenhouse system			Conventional barn		
Priming and varieties	Curing time days	Fuel used liters per kg tobacco	Primings and varieties	Curing time days	Fuel used liters per kg tobacco
Second primings for NC 95, NC 2326, and Coker 319	6	0.893	First priming Coker 319 and plot tobacco	7	1.135
Third primings for NC 2326, Coker 319, and G 28	7	0.567	First priming Coker 319 and plot tobacco	7	0.926
Upper 1/3 stalk for NC 2326 and G 28	7	0.542	Upper 1/2 stalk for Coker 319, NC 2326, and plot tobacco	6	1.052
Upper 1/3 stalk for Coker 319 and G 28	6.5	0.634			
		Average 0.659			Average 1.038

sources consumed for space heating is 1.83×10^{15} kJ (1.73×10^{15} Btu), most of it supplied by fuel oil, utility gas, and LPG (Table IV-15).[10] Rural homes will depend more on fuel oil and LPG because they are less likely to be near a utility gas pipeline.

Table IV-15. Energy sources and consumption for U.S. heating systems, 1968[10]

Fuel type	Energy 10^{13} kJ	% of total
Fuel oil	64.8	35.5
Utility gas	47.5	26.0
Liquified gas (LPG)	33.4	18.3
Electricity	17.0	9.3
Coal	10.8	5.9
Wood	8.0	4.4
None	0.7	0.4
Other	0.4	0.2
Total	182.6	100.0

Since requirements for greenhouse and residential heating vary widely depending on size, geographical location, design, construction, and personal preference, many types of combined greenhouse-residence systems are being constructed and tested. The major problems encountered to date are associated with the common open wall or door between the two structures. A primary example is insect control. Chemicals that can control insects on the plants in the greenhouse may be annoying or hazardous to residents, but thousands of uncontrolled insects might be more troublesome. Another problem is that the high humidity necessary for maximum plant growth at certain seasons of the year can cause difficulties such as mildew in the dwelling. Also, greenhouse temperatures may rise to well over 38°C (100°F) in the daytime, requiring ventilation to the outside to prevent harm to plants. This wastes heat and reduces system efficiency. Such problems must be solved, perhaps by seasonal plant production, for the greenhouse-residence solar system to be successful.

Of the many possible designs, the add-on or retrofit greenhouse connected to the side or back of a dwelling at a common wall is probably the most common. One such greenhouse, made of a redwood frame with acrylic glazing, heats an office on all but extremely cloudy days and also produces about 272 kg (600 lb) of assorted vegetables per year.[11] The solar collector for the 17.4-m² (187-ft²) greenhouse consists of a venetian blind mounted on the south wall. Although other absorber types can be used with this clear-view system, the venetian blind allows a variety of operating modes. Analysis based on a $3000 projected installation cost, including labor, 10% inflation in cost of electricity, 6% general inflation, and a 20-year 9% mortgage, gives the solar heating system a distinct advantage over an all-electric system without a greenhouse.

Nighttime insulation of the greenhouse with materials such as foam or blankets reduces heat loss and improves efficiency. Energy storage, for example, in rockbeds, soil, or water, is also cost effective and extends heating capacity. When combined with good energy conservation practices and appropriate design and operation, the greenhouse-residence solar heating system can significantly reduce fuel use.

GREENHOUSES

References

1. R.D. Cummins and G.J. Cummins, "Solar Heating of Commercial Greenhouses," *Proceedings Third Annual Conference on Solar Energy for Heating of Greenhouses and Greenhouse-Residence Combinations,* pp. 101-103, Colorado State University, Ft. Collins, April 1978.
2. Kenneth L. Goldsberry, "Insolation Available in Commercial Greenhouses," *ibid.*
3. Davis Straub, Elizabeth Coppinger, and David Bylon, "Modeling the Performance of a Passively-Heated Parabolic Aquaculture/Greenhouse," *ibid.,* pp. 93-97.
4. Carl E. Nielson and Ari Rabl, *Operation of a Small Salt Gradient Solar Pond,* Extended Abstract, International Solar Energy Society Meeting, 1975.
5. T.H. Short, P.C. Badger, and W.L. Roller, "A Solar Pond for Heating Greenhouses and Rural Residences," *Proceedings Conference on Solar Energy for Heating Greenhouses and Greenhouse-Residence Combinations,* pp. 220-233, U.S. Dept. of Energy, Cleveland, Ohio, March 1977.

6. B.K. Huang, C.F. Abrams, Jr., L.L. Coats, and C.G. Bowers, *Development of Greenhouse Bulk Curing System for Solar Energy Utilization and Plant Bed Mechanization,* Paper No. 75-1018, American Society of Agricultural Society of Agricultural Engineers, St. Joseph, Michigan, 1975.
7. C.G. Bowers, B.K. Huang, and C.F. Abrams, Jr., *Solar Energy Utilization in a Bulk Curing Greenhouse System,* Paper No. 75-3504, American Society of Agricultural Engineers, St. Joseph, Michigan, 1975.
8. Charles C. Smith, "Construction and Operation of a Solar Heated Residence/Greenhouse Combination," *loc cit* in reference 4, pp. 53-78.
9. U.S. Census of Housing 1970, Detailed Housing Characteristics, Final Report HC(1)B-1, U.S. Summary, U.S. Dept. of Commerce, Washington, D.C., 1972.
10. J.C. Fisher, *Energy Crisis in Perspective,* p. 153, Wiley, New York, 1968.
11. T.L. Thompson, Merle J. Jenson, John F. Peck, and Carl N. Hodges, "Environmental Control and Vegetable Production in a Combined Solar Collector-Greenhouse," *loc cit* in reference 1, pp. 5-16.

Grain and Crop Drying

Field drying of most grain and forage crops has been accepted practice since commercial farming began. However, sun and wind are the primary drying agents and may not be available when most needed. Crops in areas of heavy rainfall are especially subject to weather damage if not harvested in time. Wind damage is also common. Severe winds can cause lodging of crops and heavy losses at harvest due to reduced quality and poor harvesting conditions. As the demand grew for higher quality farm products, mechanical drying or curing became widespread.

Drying crops away from the field allowed farmers to follow a more predictable schedule in harvesting and, in some cases, to produce a second crop on the same land because of early removal of the first crop. Now drying and curing costs are rising rapidly because the prices of commonly used fossil fuels and electricity are increasing faster than the general inflation rate. Integration of solar energy into conventional systems may replace or reduce the demand for depletable energy sources.

Grain drying in storage requires large volumes of air at ambient or moderately elevated temperatures. In most cases, some degree of temperature fluctuation does not significantly affect grain or crop quality.[1] Simple, single-glazed solar collection systems have been used to slightly raise the temperature of drying intake air, thus speeding up the drying process. However, the relatively large investment required to install a solar system presents problems in the drying of some grains. For example, corn requires more drying energy than most grains and is dried only in the fall for a short 6–8 week period. Use for such a short time makes a solar system prohibitively costly in many instances. Solar heating systems must serve more energy needs than grain drying alone to be cost effective.

Effective use of solar energy for grain and crop drying depends on:[2]

geographical location

crop type

size of the operation

governmental economic policy

attitude of the owner-operator

Geographical location, for example, affects the availability of solar radiation at harvest time, although sunshine is generally plentiful from May to October in the United States (see Section II). Relative humidity is more variable and presents problems, particularly in the southeastern states.

Crop type is significant in drying considerations because different grain and crop species are harvested at different seasons and have different physical properties, such as mass diffusivity and thermal conductivity, that affect drying rates and determine the air conditions required to achieve safe moisture equilibrium. Early corn and soybeans can be dried in many areas with ambient air, but late crops require added heat. Peanuts must be picked while still somewhat moist to prevent losses during harvest, but then special care must be taken in storage to prevent mold growth and generation of mycotoxins. This is true of all stored crops with a high moisture content.

The size of the drying operation must accommodate the size of the crop so that the harvest can proceed in an orderly manner. Small farmers who use custom harvesting sometimes have inadequate drying capacity which can result in an interrupted harvest or spoilage of grain that is too wet.

Government has an essential role to play in the future of solar drying. At present, solar systems are not readily accepted by potential users because most of the systems are not economically competitive with conventional fuels. A government-financed economic trade-off program may be necessary to encourage greater use of solar energy for crop drying and other low-temperature processes. Such government action will have a positive influence on the attitude of the potential owner-operator of a solar dryer.

United States farms produce corn, wheat, soybeans, rice, oats, barley, and several minor types of grain. These crops are harvested and dried from spring to late fall. Since this is also a period when heat is least needed for other farm uses of solar energy such as livestock buildings, greenhouses, and other production units, multiple use of a solar system is feasible.

When early grain crops, such as wheat in the U.S. midwest, are harvested on time, second crops such as soybeans can be produced on the same land. Every day's delay in planting the second crop significantly reduces yields, so harvesting must be completed quickly.

The varied energy requirements for drying and curing different crops requires discussion specific to each crop. The following sections treat solar drying separately for each of the most economically important crops.

Rice

Solar heat used for deep-bed rice drying reduces drying time and electric fan energy consumption compared with drying by unheated air.[3] Stirring and heating slightly reduce milling yield but eliminate sharply defined drying zones by making moisture content uniform throughout the bin. Vertical stirring augers lift rice from near the bottom of the bin and deposit it on top, continuously exposing new surfaces to the drying air. Automated augers also move around the bin, thus making contact with more of the rice and preventing wet spots.

The solar collector in this system had the form of a shallow trough, 14.6 m (48 ft) long, 1.2 m (4 ft) wide, and 15.2 cm (6 in) deep, made of black-painted corrugated metal sheets backed by 7.6 cm (3 in) of glass wool insulation and glazed with clear corrugated fiberglass. Collectors had a north-south orientation and were slightly raised at one end to face south. The system initially had no heat storage. Air was drawn by fan from the collector into the drying bin at an average rate of 30.6 m^3/min (1080 cfm) against a static pressure of 6.35 cm (2.5 in) of H_2O in a 2.4-m (8-ft) depth of rice. Flow rate was slightly higher in bins with stirrers and slightly lower in those without. Average daily temperature rise during a 10-hr-per-day collection period over several days of a drying operation was approximately 5.6°C (10°F).

Table IV-16 shows the results of drying tests with and without solar heating and with and without stirring. Drying times were shorter for bins receiving solar-heated air. Although moisture content varied more widely in bins without stirrers, these bins can dry adequately if the air flow rate is at least 0.35 m^3/min per 100 kg (5.6 cfm/cwt) of rice, the initial moisture content does not exceed 20%, depth of fill is limited to a maximum of 2.4 m (8 ft), and the daily average temperature rise is no more than 5.6°C (10°F).

Energy storage was then tried to assure a uniform temperature rise during drying. Storage consisted of a corrugated steel bin 2.74 m (9 ft) in diameter and 3.35 m (11 ft) high, fitted with a perforated metal floor 45.7 cm (18 in) above the bottom, insulated with a glass-wool blanket 3.8 cm (1.5 in) thick, and filled with about 20,770 kg (22.9 tons) of 3.8-cm (1.5-in) diameter pebbles. (Pebble packing density was approximately 1281 kg/m^3, or 80 lb/ft^3). A flat-plate collector with 29.7 m^2 (320 ft^2) of absorber surface was placed along the south wall of the bins and inclined toward the south at a 22.5° angle above the horizontal, approximately the optimal inclination

Table IV-16. Effect of solar heat and stirring on rice-drying energy requirements and milling yield

Starting date	Variety	Dryer	Treatment		Moisture content		Fill depth m (ft)	Elapsed drying time days	Fan operation time hr	Electrical energy used kwhr	Milling yield*	
			Solar heat	Stirring	Initial %	Final %					Control %	Dryer-dried %
08/23/75	Bluebelle	3	Yes	Yes	16.6	11.4	2.3 (7.5)	16	117	326	60.1	59.3
08/22/75	Bluebelle	2	No	No	15.2	11.8	2.1 (7.0)	31	213	275	60.0	59.6
08/19/76	Labelle	1	Yes	No	19.6	12.0	2.4 (7.8)	15	206	221	61.5	61.5
08/19/76	Labelle	2	No	No	19.6	12.0	2.5 (8.3)	20	259	326	61.5	63.0
08/18/76	Labelle	3	Yes	Yes	16.0	12.0	2.2 (7.2)	10	139	231	60.2	60.3
08/17/76	Labelle	4	No	Yes**	16.0	12.0	2.16 (7.1)	19	246	321	60.2	60.3
09/09/76	Lebonnet	3	Yes	Yes	17.8	11.5	2.16 (7.1)	16	218	292	57.0	55.7
09/29/76	Brazos	3	Yes	Yes	17.5	12.2	2.1 (7.0)	13	217	281	62.7	61.1
09/29/76	Brazos	4	No	Yes	17.5	12.2	2.0 (6.7)	20	278	377	62.7	61.7

*Whole kernels of milled rice.
**Because of breakdowns, stirring auger operated only 7 days.

Table IV-17. Air flow rate in rice dryers

Dryer	Date	Stirring	Fill depth m (ft)	Plenum static pressure kPa	Exit air velocity m/min	Calculated air flow rate* by static pressure m³/min	by velocity m³/min
1	07/28/77	No	2.4 (7.9)	0.61	123.7	27.0	26.7
2	07/28/77	No	2.28 (7.5)	0.70	136.5	30.6	29.4
3	07/28/77	Yes	2.2 (7.2)	0.66	161.5	33.3	33.9
4	07/28/77	Yes	2.19 (7.2)	0.48	158.5	27.0	34.1
1	10/17/77	No	2.5 (8.2)	0.62	128.0	27.0	27.6
2	10/17/77	No	2.4 (7.9)	0.72	145.1	31.7	31.3
3	10/17/77	Yes	2.25 (7.4)	0.67	162.8	33.1	34.0
4	10/17/77	Yes	2.25 (7.4)	0.55	149.9	28.8	32.3

*Air flow/ft² was obtained from pressure drop/ft depth by reference to appropriate graphs and converted to metric units. Top openings were 2.32 ft² for dryers 1, 2, and 4 and 2.26 ft² for dryer 3.

Table IV-18. Effect of solar heat and stirring on rice (Labelle) drying energy requirements and milling yield

Starting date	Dryer	Treatment Solar heat	Stirring	Moisture content Initial %	Final %	Drying time days	Fan operating time hr	Electrical energy used kwhr	Milling yield Whole kernels, % (Total milled, %) Air-dried	Dryer-dried
07/22/77	1	Yes	No	19.0	11.5	12	230	211	60.4 (68.0)	61.1 (68.4)
07/22/77	2	No	No	19.0	12.1	31	315	297	57.2 (66.5)	61.1 (68.5)
07/22/77	3	Yes	Yes	19.2	11.5	11	186	311	58.5 (66.2)	60.4 (68.1)
07/21/77	4*	Yes	Yes	21.0	12.0	10	245	325	59.7 (67.4)	62.1 (68.9)
10/17/77	1	Yes	No	18.9	11.3	24	322	305	60.0 (69.3)	61.5 (70.3)
10/15/77	2	No	No	20.0	11.5	30	403	399	61.9 (70.0)	62.5 (70.6)
10/14/77	3	Yes	Yes	21.2	12.2	24	359	453	60.8 (69.2)	60.2 (69.8)
10/14/77	4*	Yes	Yes	21.9	12.2	14	367	426	61.5 (69.6)	60.1 (69.3)

*Pebble-bed storage.

for collecting solar radiation at 30°N latitude in August. The collector was constructed of locally available materials for $14.64/m² ($1.36/ft²) of surface area. Total system cost was $2551.

Four tests were then run under various drying conditions. All dryers were filled with the Labelle variety of early maturing, long grain rice between July 21 and 23, emptied after the drying period, and refilled with second-crop rice between October 14 and 17. Air to dryers 1 and 3 was solar heated directly by the trough collectors without storage. Air to dryer 2 was unheated. Air to dryer 4 was solar heated in passing through the flat-plate collector and the pebble-bed storage on its way into and through the rice bed and out the top of the drying bin. Rice in dryers 1 and 2 was not stirred. Rice in dryers 3 and 4 was stirred with a vertical auger for 9 hours each day.

Composite samples of rice were taken during loading and unloading to determine initial and final moisture content and drying was stopped when moisture reached approximately 12%. All rice was then milled by standard procedures and inspected for the yield of whole kernels. Table IV-17 shows system parameters and calculated air flow rates. Table IV-18 shows drying test results.

Drying methods had little effect on rice milling quality. Although dryer 4 required the least drying time, it saved little or no energy and did not justify the cost of the pebble heat-storage bed. Average daily energy outputs in kilowatt hours (kwhr) of the three solar collectors for July and October were, respectively: dryer 1 – 34 and 20; dryer 3 – 38 and 21; and dryer 4 – 68 and 47.

Corn

Picker-sheller combines require harvesting of corn at a high moisture content to minimize field losses due to shattering of grain. However, the corn must then be mechanically dried for safe storage. Ambient, high-temperature, or solar-heated air is used as needed.

High temperature air is used frequently because it considerably shortens the drying period. However, high heat often damages the grain and uses large quantities of fossil fuels. Ambient air reduces heat damage, but may leave unsafe moisture levels and grain quality may deteriorate during the long drying time. Fungal invasion of newly harvested corn is an ever-present problem which may be aggravated by inefficient drying methods. An appropriate combination of initial, short-term, high-temperature drying and extended, lower-temperature, final drying can save energy and maintain higher grain quality.

Methods of applying solar energy to corn drying include regeneration of desiccants such as silica gel or over-dried corn; moderately increasing the drying-air temperature by about 7°C (12°F) above ambient and reducing the ventilation rate; combining a conventional heat source for high-temperature predrying to about a 20% moisture content with a solar heat source for low-temperature final drying; and using a plastic cover or special construction to enable solar radiation to warm the air in the drying building.

Koh[4] showed that it is technically feasible to regenerate silica gel with solar heat to store the energy as drying potential rather than as a heat source. The regenerated desiccant draws moisture from the passing air which then continues with a lower relative humidity and faster drying action through the corn bin (Figure IV-17).

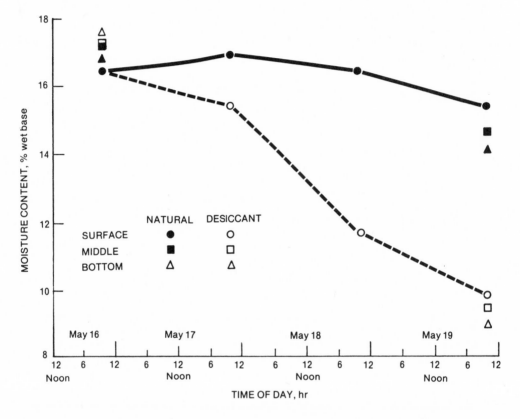

Figure IV-17. *Natural vs desiccant drying of corn at various bin depths*

Corn-bin design allows the use of desiccated or ambient air separately or in combination (Figure IV-18). The proportion of desiccated air is increased as the ambient relative humidity rises above 60%. This method has the major advantage that moisture removal from the air is easier to control than addition of heat.

In corn and milo drying trials with regenerated silica gel[5], drying time decreased and fungus problems were somewhat alleviated. Moist kernels were initially invaded by Fusarium (44%), Penicillium (27%), Rhizapus (20%), Aspergillus flavus (12%), and A. niger (15%). All increased during the drying period and to the same extent

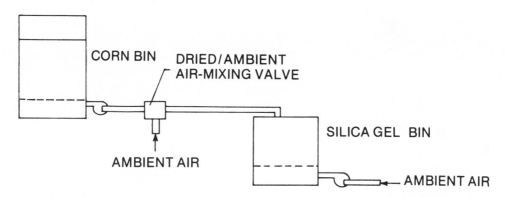

Figure IV-18. *Corn dryer with provision for adding desiccated air to ambient air stream as ambient relative humidity rises*

with desiccated air as with the ambient air used to dry the controls. Penicillium and A. niger multiplied more than the other fungi, and A. flavus infected an average of 38% of the dried kernels. However, the shorter drying time with desiccated air limited the accumulation of aflatoxin B_1 to a final concentration of 13 ppb, well below the 20-ppb FDA guideline, while the concentration in naturally dried corn reached 37 ppb.

Use of the desiccant saved very little energy because of the electricity needed to operate fans for desiccant regeneration and air drying. However, the shorter drying times and reduction in fungal toxins make desiccant regeneration with solar heat an attractive alternative to consumption of fossil fuels for accelerating corn drying. The desiccant had no apparent effect on susceptibility to corn breakage which seems related only to moisture content.

When corn is stored on the farm during summer, solar drying is efficient because air temperatures are higher and humidity lower than in fall and winter. Summer-stored corn can be overdried and then used as a desiccant, like regenerated silica gel, for fall-harvested corn.[6] In tests, overdried corn filled 20% of the bin and was overlaid with fresh moist corn. A single-auger stirrer mixed the two. For a test control, a conventional bin without an auger was filled to the same depth with fresh corn only. Drying procedures were otherwise the same for both except that the conventional system had a heater not included in the desiccant drying system.

Test results in Table IV-19 show that the combination of desiccant and low-temperature air for drying corn used significantly less electrical energy than the conventional system did. Grain qualities were equal.

Tests of various sequences of high-temperature drying to a moisture content of about 20% followed by long-term low-temperature drying with solar heat indicate that the low-temperature final drying can be very effective when ambient

Table IV-19. Corn drying using overdried summer-stored corn as a desiccant (bins filled October 11-14, 1977, axial-flow fans operated continuously)

	Desiccant bin	Conventional bin
Initial moisture content, %		
Desiccant corn	11.7	—
Wet corn (new harvest)	23.3	23.1
Combined	20.8	—
Final moisture, %	14.7	15.3
Drying time, days	87	41
Fan rating, kw	0.75	3.7
Aeration rate, m^3/min per m^3 of corn in bin	0.63	1.4
Stirrer rating, kw	1.1	None
Stirrer operation, days		
Continuous	1-15	—
8 AM to 4:30 PM	16-87	—
Heater rating, kw	None	2.4
Heater operation	—	Continuous
Energy consumption, kwhr		
Fan: Desiccant preparation	52	—
Fall & spring drying	1954	6232
Stirrer	873	—
Heater	—	2341
Total	2879	8573
Energy consumption, $kwhr/m^3$ of grain added in fall per % pt moisture reduction	4.3	9.9
Maximum electrical demand, $kw/1000~m^3$ grain added in fall	24.7	84.6

temperature and relative humidity are suitable. When field conditions permit natural drying to the 20% moisture level, the high-temperature phase is not needed.

The effectiveness of low-temperature drying, using air no more than 3°C (5.4°F) warmer than ambient, depends on air flow rate, initial moisture content, and weather conditions. Table IV-20 shows the air flow rates required for adequate corn drying under different conditions of mositure content and local climate, determined by computer simulation.[7] Required flow rates increase from the cool, dry regions around North Dakota to the warm humid regions of central Indiana and Ohio. Also, drying time is longer in southern than in northern regions.

Table IV-20. Minimum air flow rates, in m³/min per m³ of grain, required to dry corn with less than 0.5% dry-matter loss, derived from computer simulations for next-to-worst year based on 10 years of weather data for various geographic locations

Starting date	October 1				October 15				November 1			
Initial moisture content, %	20	22	24	26	20	22	24	26	20	22	24	26
Bismarck, ND	0.233	0.442	1.037	2.019	0.249	0.345	0.458	1.045	0.289	0.394	0.482	0.707
Lincoln, NB	0.748	1.439	2.453	3.418	0.345	0.933	1.665	3.121	0.370	0.530	0.868	1.793
Columbia, MO	0.643	1.399	2.453	4.207	0.434	1.142	1.994	3.845	0.345	0.659	1.423	2.236
Indianapolis, IN	1.890	2.324	4.512	7.649	0.933	1.665	3.298	4.343	0.764	1.528	2.831	2.869
Midland, TX	0.740	1.616	2.855	4.886	0.514	1.045	2.220	3.692	0.273	0.659	1.367	2.260
Macon, GA	1.166	3.088	5.325	9.950	0.802	2.083	3.555	5.751	0.587	1.335	2.107	4.890

Notes: (1) Minimum recommended flow rate is 0.603 m³/min-m³; lower rates are considered aerating not drying. (2) Simulation assumes a 2°C temperature rise due to a continuous heat supply and an additional 1°C due to heat produced by the fan motor.

Generally, the study indicated: 1) drying time is more predictable if heat is added; 2) energy requirements are highest for systems using continuous heat from a conventional source, lowest for solar-supplemented systems; 3) overdrying is a greater problem if heat is added; 4) dry-matter decomposition is reduced if heat is added or if corn is dryer when harvested; and 5) overall costs are highest for solar-supplemented systems. Low-temperature drying procedures with solar heating now require careful management to be satisfactory for drying corn, but will be more widely used if energy costs and availability continue to be major problems.

Solar energy can also be captured to accelerate corn drying with an inexpensive greenhouse-type enclosure covered with clear plastic film. Such drying of early harvested corn in Indiana added $2000 above drying costs to the market value.[8]

Steps in building and using the enclosure were:

1. A 6-mil black plastic film was laid on slightly sloping ground to prevent ground moisture from rising into the drying corn.

2. Recycled shipping pallets were placed on the plastic ground cloth about 10 cm (4 in) apart and covered with plastic netting (similar to ½-in mesh hardware screening) to form a hollow floor with a perforated top surface.

3. Used power poles were laid in a 7.6 x 28.6-m (25 x 94-ft) rectangle on top of the outermost pallets to define a border from under which the pallet ends protrude.

4. One of the shorter end poles was raised onto 0.6-m (2-ft) high posts and plywood was nailed against this framework to make a 7.6 x 0.6-m (25 x 2-ft) end wall containing a 0.6 x 0.6-m (2 x 2-ft) access door (normally closed) and an opening for installation of the discharge ducts from squirrel-cage blowers.

5. The load of corn to be dried was piled on the mesh-covered pallets and covered with clear polyethylene which was then attached to the border poles.

6. The blowers were turned on and created a positive pressure of about 0.06 kPa (0.25 in of water) in the enclosure that caused the clear plastic sheet to billow up into a paraboloid and forced about 113 m³/min (4000 cfm) of air down through the grain into the hollow pallets and out the perimeter.

With proper management, this system dried and stored corn for $6.50/m³ (22.9¢/bu) to which fuel and oil for the gasoline-operated blowers added less than 3¢/bu, thus indicating an energy-efficient process. Problems were minor, including some overdrying around the edges of the pile and sprouting of a few bushels due to condensation. In general, the system proved to be cost effective and promises to be an economical application of solar energy to low-temperature drying of corn.

Peanuts

Peanuts are a valuable source of protein and oil and must be harvested while quite moist to preserve quality and minimize field losses due to shattering. The nuts are exposed by digging and then usually dried for a short time in the windrow before being picked. After harvest, which usually occurs in September and October, moisture content should be reduced about 0.5%/hr to 10% or less. Most drying systems now use large quantities of LPG fuel.

Edible peanuts require careful drying because continuous exposure to temperatures above 35°C (95°F) causes an off-taste and may split a high percentage of kernels. On the other hand, low-temperature drying or interruption of a high-temperature drying cycle encourages mold growth and increases the risk of mycotoxin development.

General recommendations for peanut drying include: limiting drying air temperature to 25°C (95°F) maximum, but also to a temperature no more than 8°C

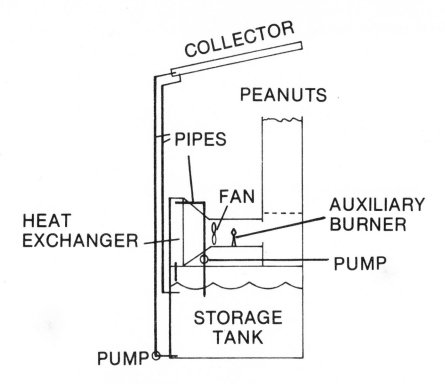

Figure IV-19. *Peanut dryer with solar-heated water*

(14°F) above ambient, and maintaining a minimum air flow rate of 12.5 m³/min per m³(12.5 cfm/ft³) of peanuts in the dryer.

Several feasibility studies of solar-assisted peanut-drying units have been conducted. Troeger and Butler[9] compared a water (Figure IV-19) and an air (Figure IV-20) solar system with a conventional LPG dryer. Initially, four types of collectors

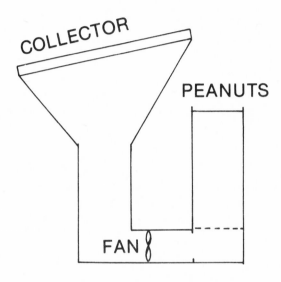

Figure IV-20. *Peanut dryer with solar-heated air*

(Figure IV-21) were mounted on the roof of the steel frame building and energy was stored in water, but drain-down problems and freeze damage necessitated modifications (Figure IV-22). Table IV-21 shows the relative effectiveness of the collection systems.

The collector for the solar air system of Figure IV-20 consisted of galvanized sheet-metal panels riveted to the Z-bars supporting the roof of an existing building to form a duct 5 cm (2 in) deep, backed underneath with styrofoam insulation. The air system had no storage and intake air temperature was not regulated.

Table IV-22 shows the test results. A measure of drying performance is the relative amounts of split and sound kernels among the dried peanuts. The greater the percentage of split kernels, the greater the chance of fungal penetration. Both water and air systems performed well. The water system supplied 60-70% of all required energy, and the air system fluctuated between 20% and 100%. Such variability is common in solar systems without storage.

Total energy requirements, as well as the specific energy input (SEI) in kJ/g of water removed, varied with the peanuts' initial moisture content and with ambient

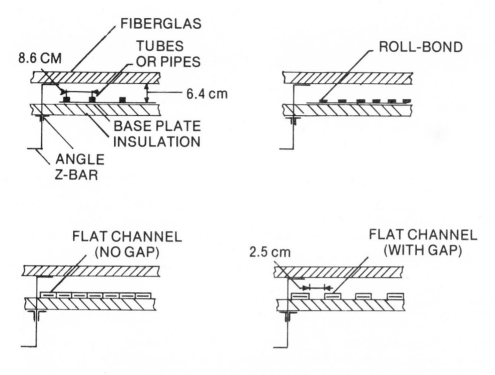

Figure IV-21. *Initial (1975) collector types with water channels for peanut-drying tests*

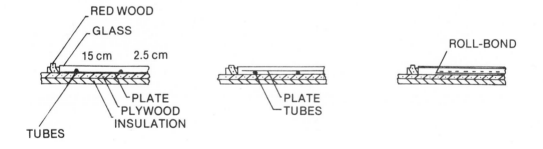

Figure IV-22. *Modified (1976) collector types with water channels for peanut-drying tests*

temperatures. Figures IV-23 and IV-24 show the results of several trials of the two solar-assisted systems and of an LPG-fired process. The rise in SEI for lower initial moisture content indicates that residual water molecules are bound more tightly in drier peanuts. The drop in SEI for lower ambient temperatures (lower vapor pressures in the air) indicates that the greater difference between internal and external vapor pressures facilitates the drying action.

Table IV-21. Peanut-drying effectiveness of various rooftop water solar collectors relative to copper Roll-bond type, based on measured heat gain across collector

Water duct	Dimensions, cm Inside tube	Spacing on centers	Relative effectiveness
1975 Collectors set on unpainted 18-gauge (0.12-cm) black-iron sheet metal base			
Galvanized pipe[1]	1.58	8.6	0.73
Black pipe[1]	1.58	8.6	0.75
Copper tubing[1]	1.12	8.6	0.34
Copper Roll-bond[2]	1.17 × 0.40	2.5	1.00
Flat aluminum (closely packed)[3]	4.65 × 0.64	5.1	0.69
Flat aluminum (5-cm spacing)[3]	4.65 × 0.64	10.1	1.35
1976 Collectors painted smooth flat black, no thermal bonding of external pipes			
Copper Roll-bond[2]	1.17 × 0.40	2.5	1.00
Pipe above plate	1.58	15	0.72
Pipe below plate	1.58	15	0.54

[1]Unpainted, thermally bonded to collector plate with high-temperature grease.
[2]Painted flat black, commercially available as integral tube within sheet heat exchanger.
[3]Channels painted dull smooth black.

Table IV-22. Milling quality of solar-dried peanuts, given as percent sound split kernels

Test	Solar-dried Water collector Top	Bottom	Air collector Top	Bottom	Conventionally dried Top	Bottom
75–1	2.5a	3.1a	2.1a	2.5a	2.3a	2.3a
76–1	—	—	1.1a	1.6b	1.5b	1.5b
76–2	2.1a	2.5a	3.1b	3.7c	2.3a	2.2a
76–3	2.2ab	3.7c	1.7a	2.6b	—	—
76–4	1.7a	2.5bc	2.1ab	2.8c	2.0a	2.6bc
76–5	2.7a	4.5c	2.5a	3.8b	2.4a	4.0bc

Percentages with the same small letter (a, b, or c) within a given test (on the same line of the table) do not differ significantly at the 5% probability level. Letter pairs (e.g., ab) indicate percentages that lie between two statistically distinct milling quality levels (a and b). Data from different tests (different lines of the table) are not comparable with each other.

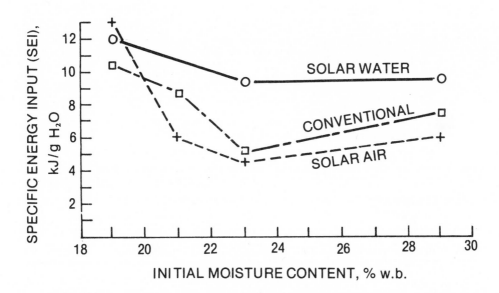

Figure IV-23. *Effect of initial peanut moisture content on required drying energy*

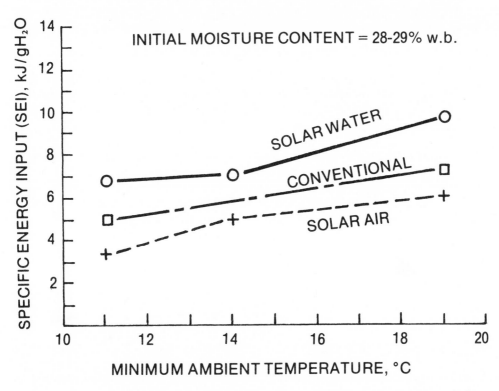

Figure IV-24. *Effect of minimum ambient temperature on energy required for peanut drying*

A solar energy system like the one studied, equipped with a 70-m² (750-ft²) collector and a 7570-liter (2000-gal) water storage, can supply 75% of the energy needed to dry 4080 kg (4.5 tons) of peanuts from an initial moisture content of 20% to a desired 10% level in 24 hours. As with other types of grain and crop drying, its economic feasibility will be greatly enhanced by multiple use.

Tobacco

Supplemental heat has been used for many years to control the drying and curing rate of crops, especially tobacco. Although curing procedures differ for the various tobacco types such as burley, flue-cured, and dark-fired, all include a period of moisture removal from the leaf. They may also include a special heating period to promote desired chemical changes.

Curing takes place in a tobacco barn designed, built, and managed specifically for the tobacco type being cured. Curing of burley relies heavily on naturally occurring air temperatures and relative humidity, but burley curing, like the curing of other tobacco varieties, may also involve supplemental heating, usually burning of fossil fuels, to speed drying and establish the temperatures for special leaf-curing cycles.

Adverse weather conditions, especially high humidity, can drastically affect the quality of tobacco leaves. If humidity is too high to allow an acceptable drying and curing rate, added heat is essential to increase the drying potential of the air and prevent deterioration of leaf quality.

The recommended amount of supplemental heat for the conventional burley tobacco barn is approximately 145 kw/ha (200,000 Btu/hr per acre)[10], or as much as 1136 liter (300 gal) of LPG fuel per acre of cropland. The LPG can be replaced with solar energy.

Several methods of collecting and applying solar energy to tobacco drying and curing have been used successfully. Multiple-use greenhouses described above and roof-mounted or free-standing solar collectors combined with rock or liquid storage systems (similar to those used for grain drying) have all worked well. However, solar supplementation must be managed properly and adapted to and integrated with conventional curing systems to ensure high product quality.

Hay

Hay crops are normally cured in the field before being baled for storage. However, some types of hay, such as alfalfa, may be ground and used in feed for high-cost rations. Also, when weather conditions prevent field drying, heat-assisted curing in storage may be economically warranted.

Hay curing in storage has been tried with limited success. It requires the consumption of large quantities of fuel which might be reduced by drawing on solar sources.

Although solar technology developed for grain drying and greenhouse heating should be applicable to hay curing, curing hay in storage is such a marginally cost-effective practice that it has attracted little solar research.

GRAIN AND CROP DRYING

References

1. George H. Foster and Robert M. Peart, "Solar Energy for Grain Drying," *Proceedings Solar Grain Drying Conference,* pp. 1-3, Purdue University, West Lafayette, Indiana, May 1978.
2. R.N. Misra and H.M. Keener, "Solar Grain Drying for Ohio," *ibid,* pp. 13-28.
3. D.A. Calderwood, "Bin-drying with Stirring Rice," *ibid.*
4. H.K. Koh, *Study on the Use of Solar Energy for the Regeneration of Silica Gel Used in Grain Drying,* Ph.D. dissertation, Kansas State University, Manhattan, 1977.
5. D.F. Aldis, R. Burroughs, and J.W. Hughes, "Solar Regeneration of Silica Gel and Use in Grain Drying," *loc cit* in reference 1, pp. 37-56.
6. C.J. Bern, M.E. Anderson, and W.F. Wilcke, "Solar Drying of Corn with a Desiccant/Low Temperature System," *ibid,* pp. 57-60.
7. T.L. Thompson and R.O. Pierce, "Solar and Natural Air Grain Dryer Performance in the Corn Producing Areas of the U.S., Simulation Results," *ibid,* pp. 119-134.
8. Robert J. Buker, "Inflated Plastic Structures for Solar Drying of Grain," *ibid,* pp. 91-88.
9. J.M. Troeger and J.L. Butler, "Solar Drying of Peanuts in Georgia," *Proceedings Solar Grain Drying Conference,* pp. 32-43, Weaver Laboratory, North Carolina University, Raleigh, June 1977.
10. L.R. Walton, W.H. Henson, Jr., S.G. McNeill, J.N. Walker, B.F. Parker, and Joe M. Bunn, "Curing Burley Tobacco with Solar Energy," *ibid,* pp. 107-116.

Energy-Intensive Applications

Certain energy-intensive practices in agriculture and food systems have been associated with the rapid rise in food and fiber production in the United States and other developed countries. These practices enable a relatively small acreage to yield vast amounts of farm products. Prominent among such practices are:

> Irrigation of formerly unproductive or marginal lands.

> Intensive, controlled-environment food production in confined areas such as large greenhouse complexes or aquaculture (fish and seafood production) facilities.

> Extensive processing, preservation, and storage of food products.

Machine power, depending mainly on fossil fuels, has supplanted human labor in most of these areas of concentrated effort. Although the entire food production and processing industry accounts for only a small fraction of the total energy used in the United States, an energy shortage would drastically reduce the quality and quantity of food unless alternate sources were found. Direct and indirect use of the sun's radiation for agricultural applications can provide such an alternate source.

Intensive commercial agriculture requires energy in the form of electricity to operate irrigation pumps, feed and fertilizer milling machinery, processing equipment, and food preservation and storage systems. It also uses heat to control the environment in large production facilities, raise the temperature of industrial process water, generate steam, and assist in the conversion of biomass into usable forms of energy. Electricity may be generated on-site by solar-thermal conversion (STC) or by photovoltaic devices which transform radiation directly into electricity. STC is the most common method at present, using both central receiver and distributed types of solar systems.[1]

Irrigation

Irrigation is a major consumer of energy expended for agricultural production, requiring the equivalent of 30–300 liter (8–80 gal) of gasoline per acre-foot of water pumped, depending on the water location and source. About 14 million hectares (34-35 million acres) of United States farmland is irrigated out of a total of approximately 162 million hectares (400 million acres). In 1975, 20% of all farm production was attributed to irrigated farms.[2] Most of this land would produce little without irrigation.

Most of the irrigation is found in Washington, Oregon, California, Idaho, Nevada, Utah, Arizona, Montana, Wyoming, Colorado, New Mexico, North and South Dakota, Nebraska, Kansas, Oklahoma, Texas, Louisiana, and Florida. Other agricultural states also use irrigation, particularly for specialty crops, but rely primarily on the generally adequate annual rainfall for good crop production.

In some instances, water from surface sources will flow by gravity directly onto fields to be irrigated, requiring little expenditure of energy. In most states, however, energy is necessary to pump irrigation water from wells or impoundments. The amount of energy required depends on the lift or pressure needed and the type of irrigation, for example, ditch, flood, or sprinkler. Irrigation systems are classified as shallow well, deep well, or sump basin and system specifications are usually determined by the amount of water lift needed.

An excellent working example of a sump-basin irrigation system is being developed and tested by Battelle Memorial Institute at Gila Bend, Arizona.[3] It delivers 630 liter/sec (10,000 gpm) to 10,000 hectares (25,000 acres) planted in cotton, wheat, barley, alfalfa, and safflower.[4] Its solar energy source has 511 m² (5500 ft²) of parabolic-trough, tracking collectors that heat water at their focal axis to

149°C (300°F). The hot water passes through heat exchangers, energizing the power package, and then circulates through the closed loop back to the collectors (Figure IV-25).

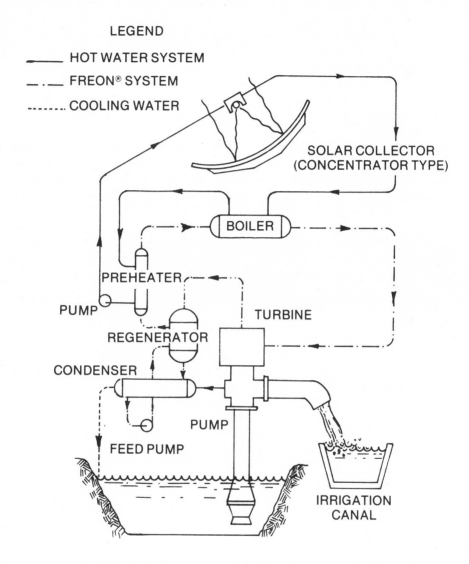

LEGEND

_____ HOT WATER SYSTEM

_ . _ FREON® SYSTEM

.... COOLING WATER

SOLAR COLLECTOR (CONCENTRATOR TYPE)

BOILER

PREHEATER

PUMP

TURBINE

REGENERATOR

CONDENSER

PUMP

FEED PUMP

IRRIGATION CANAL

Figure IV-25. *Gila River solar-powered irrigation system* (Northwestern Mutual-Battelle Memorial Institute)

The transferred heat vaporizes liquid Freon to power the Rankine-cycle turbine engine. At peak performance, the engine delivers 50 hp to the irrigation pump which lifts water about 4.3 m (14 ft) from the sump basin to the irrigation canal.

Although the system now uses electricity to power auxiliary components, it can be adapted to derive all its energy from the solar source. Economic analysis of the system is continuing.

Sandia Laboratories, Albuquerque, New Mexico have cooperated with New Mexico state engineers in a solar deep-well irrigation project in the Estancia valley.[5] This solar system has north-south oriented, parabolic-trough, tracking collectors capable of raising the temperature of the heat-transfer oil to 204–232°C (400–450°F). The oil is chemically stable because air is excluded from the closed circulation loop, and is used both for heat transfer and for heat storage in an unpressurized 22,700-liter (6000-gal) tank.

Freon 113 drives a high-speed turbine coupled to a turbine pump which lifts 42 liter/sec (670 gpm) of well water from a 34-m (112-ft) depth to a storage pond from which irrigation water is pumped. The solar-operated engine can deliver 18 kw (25 hp) at 1760 rpm. An electric backup motor of the same capacity is connected to the gearbox so that the electric and solar pumps can operate independently or together. The storage pond holds 5000 kiloliters (4 acre-ft), approximately a 60-hr irrigation supply when solar energy is not available and the deep-well pumping system is not operating. A booster pump driven by a diesel engine delivers water from the irrigation pond to two side-roll sprinkler systems.

The large capital investment for this solar system is said to demand critical management scrutiny to determine applications with the greatest potential for profitable economic returns. The system as described was designed to irrigate approximately 40 hectares (100 acres) of high-market-value crops and perhaps to heat greenhouses or supply hot water in off-seasons. Similar investment-vs-payback considerations also apply to other solar-powered irrigation systems.

Livestock Feedmills

Livestock feedmills and other types of agricultural processing facilities that require both electricity and heat are prime candidates for the application of solar energy. In 1976, J.H. Strickland[6] outlined the economic feasibility of a solar energy source for livestock feedmills. Lipps and Hildebrandt[7] reported that a central-receiver solar-collector array was selected to produce the 150°C (300°F) temperatures needed to generate process steam.

The system (Figure IV-26) can produce 340 kw of electricity and 2200 kw of heat. The 30,000-head feedmill requires 3.9 kwhr electric and 250 kwhr thermal energy per head per month for operation at full capacity. Surplus collected energy is stored as heat in a storage filled with rock and oil. When storage temperature is too low, an auxiliary heater in the collector loop can be fired to meet the energy demand. The system uses a Rankine steam-cycle turbine.

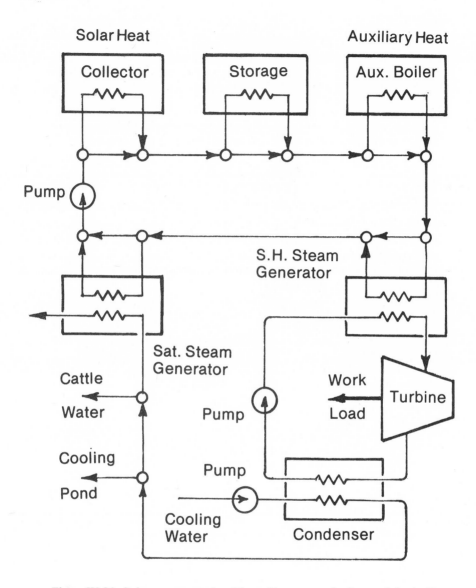

Figure IV-26. *Solar energy supply with auxiliary source for livestock feedmill*

The central receiver solar system and Rankine engine required a capital investment of $960,000. Although more efficient expander systems are needed, the present system appears to be quite competitive with conventional energy sources, based on calculated annual maintenance costs and an assumed 30-year operating life.

Steam and Hot Water

The major industries directly or indirectly related to agriculture consume about three-quarters of the energy used by all industry, or almost one-third the U.S. total for all purposes (Table IV-23).[8] Agriculture depends heavily on these industries for

Table IV-23. Energy consumption by major industrial users, 1975 data from Lawrence Livermore (Cal.) Laboratories and Federal Energy Administration

Industry	Energy used per year 10^{15} kilojoule	$(10^{15}$ Btu)	% of industrial total	% of all U.S. energy
Food & kindred products	2.9	(2.7)	8	3.3
Paper & allied products	3.2	(3.0)	9	3.7
Chemicals & allied products	7.1	(6.7)	20	8.2
Petroleum & coal products	3.9	(3.7)	11	4.5
Stone, clay & glass products	3.2	(3.0)	9	3.7
Primary metal industries	6.7	(6.4)	19	7.8
Total	26.9	(25.5)	76	31.2

equipment, supplies, and services. Energy consumed by all industry amounts to 41% of the U.S. total, including 12% and 4% for producing process steam and hot water, respectively (Table IV-24)[8], and derives almost entirely from depletable fuels (Table IV-25).[8] Steam and hot-water users, such as the pulp and paper industry, dairy producers, textile dyers and finishers, and canneries, offer good opportunities for conversion to solar heating.

A prime example of solar-energy use in an industry serving agriculture is the can-washing system installed in a Sacramento, California soup cannery.[9] Daily, 45,420 liter (12,000 gal) of well water receives initial heating as it flows through roof-mounted flat-plate collectors and then final heating in 6 parallel legs of Acurex parabolic-trough concentrating collectors, emerges at temperatures up to 90°C (195°F), and flows into a 75,700-liter (20,000-gal) storage tank. Water is pumped directly from storage to the can-washing line. An auxiliary heat exchanger automatically turns on if the storage-water temperature falls below 82°C (180°F). The solar system supplies about 74% of the energy required for a single line.

Economic feasibility is still under study, but users are optimistic about the potential for long-range energy savings.

Table IV-24. Industrial energy consumption relative to U.S. total energy usage of 86 × 10^{15} kilojoules (82 × 10^{15} Btu), 1975 estimates based on data from Lawrence Livermore Laboratories, University of California at Livermore, and Federal Energy Administration

Category	Energy used		% of U.S. total
	10^{15} kilojoules	(10^{15} Btu)	
Process hot water	3	(3)	4
Process steam	12	(11)	12
Direct combustion heating	9	(9)	11
Electrical	8	(8)	10
Miscellaneous	3	(3)	4
Total industrial consumption	35	(34)	41

Table IV-25. Estimated energy sources for industry, 1975

Source	Energy		% of total industrial use
	10^{15} kilojoule	(10^{15} Btu)	
Natural gas	16	(15)	44
Coal	9	(9)	26
Petroleum	7	(7)	21
Electricity	3	(3)	9
Total	35	(34)	100

Table IV-26. Energy consumption for process hot water at Campbell Sacramento plant

Process	Temperature °C (°F)	Yearly energy consumption 10^9 kilojoule (10^9 Btu)
Blanching	96 (205)	26 (25)
Product ingredient	99 (210)	69 (65)
Meat preparation	99 (210)	2 (2)
Can washing	82–91 (180–195)	134 (127)
Cleanup	60–71 (140–160)	48 (46)
Others	82–99 (180–210)	47 (45)
Total		326 (310)

Other cannery operations require large volumes of hot water that might also be heated with solar radiation. They include (Table IV-26) vegetable blanching, defrosting and preparation of meat and other soup ingredients, cleanup (hourly during regular work shifts and major plant cleanup during third shift), and such other procedures as hydrostatic cooking at 93°C (200°F).

Poultry and Meat Processing

Poultry and meat processing use large quantities of thermal and electrical energy for heating scald and cleanup water, making ice, refrigeration, and plant operation. An analysis of energy use in broiler production and processing in Georgia[10] showed that processing was the greatest single consumer (Table IV-27). The report states that heat reclamation from the ammonia-compressor ice system and the steam-heated scald water tank could significantly reduce energy use. Solar-heated industrial process steam and hot-water systems like the soup-cannery system described above could then be used to supply much of the remaining energy needs. Such prospects also apply to red-meat processing which has requirements and problems similar to those of poultry.

Table IV-27. 1976 energy costs, excluding transportation, for broiler production and processing in Georgia

	Energy, kJ (Btu)	Cost, ¢
Layer	20 (19)	0.013
Hatchery	330 (310)	0.170
Broiler producer	2800 (2700)	1.240
Broiler processor	3500 (3320)	1.100
Feed	1390 (1320)	0.460
Total	8040 (7669)	2.983

Manure Drying

Drying animal wastes makes them easier to handle and use and reduces annoyances such as odor and flies. These advantages have induced several manufacturers to produce commercial dryers which have been extensively tested.[11] The efficiency of representative dryers was about 50% (ratio of energy needed to evaporate water to the total consumed). The dryers use fossil fuels so operating costs can be expected to rise with fuel prices.

Various methods have been used to apply solar heating to manure drying. Deep stacking of wet manure to promote microbiological activity is sufficient for some applications, but requires large storage areas and does not reduce moisture content enough for many purposes. Spreading thin layers of manure in open sunshine encounters the ever present problems of uncertain weather and fly breeding.

Thin-layer spreading with constant agitation moderated the main problems in trials conducted with poultry manure during spring weather in southern California.[12] With a 3-day period for drying the daily manure production of 24,000 laying hens, fossil-fuel savings were 95 therms/day. A greenhouse-type cover on rainy days allowed the drying process to continue uninterrupted.

In Mississippi, a single-glazed solar roof collector supplies heat for drying thin layers of poultry manure on a moving belt.[13] The belt dryer requires a substantial capital investment and was only partially successful in early trials. As seen in Table IV-28, the manure moisture content never decreased to the desired 8–12% level (conditions were modified for various test runs listed in the table). More collector output and improved drying procedures are necessary to make this system practical.

Table IV-28. Moving belt manure drying with solar heat

Run	Air temperature, °C		Manure moisture content, %		
	Inlet	Outlet	Wet	Dry	Change
1	56.77	49.9	80.5	52.6	27.9
2	68.04	53.5	—	—	—
3	59.97	46.9	79.4	73.3	6.1
4	62.12	52.5	76.5	49.5	27.9
5	54.36	47.3	81.1	69.0	12.2
6	59.93	49.97	78.9	59.9	19.0
7	57.0	49.1	82.5	58.7	23.8
8	65.0	53.9	78.4	58.3	20.1
9	63.9	52.9	72.5	54.5	18.0
10	66.0	55.6	73.9	32.7	41.2
11	62.17	52.3	75.6	44.7	30.9

An interesting alternative to drying manure is the application of low-temperature heat to sustain digestion which produces methane gas. Such methane generation may become economically practical as other fuel costs mount.

Lumber Drying

Although drying is only one of many processing steps undergone by lumber in transition from the standing tree to the finished board, it uses the most energy, approximately 0.5 kwhr electrical and 2500 Btu (0.7 kwhr) thermal per board foot. Total annual U.S. energy consumption for lumber drying is 10^{14} Btu (about 3 x 10^{10}

kwhr). The required energy and temperature vary with the type of wood, but the general temperature range of 43–116°C (110–240°F) makes kiln drying a promising application of solar energy.

The J.A. LaCour Kiln Service is experimenting with two side-by-side continuous-horizontal-flow, wood-drying kilns near Canton, Mississippi, one heated by solar energy and the other by fossil fuel. The solar system, designed to deliver 44% of the total required energy, consists of a 232-m² (2500-ft²) collector area arranged in a sawtooth configuration with reflectors, a 4800-gal water capacity for heat transfer and storage, and finned-tube heat-exchange convectors in the kiln. Continuous duty is a particularly effective way to test solar energy applications. Although solar-heated kiln drying of lumber is still in the research stage, it shows commercial potential.

ENERGY-INTENSIVE APPLICATIONS
References

1. R.L. Gervais and Piet B. Bos, "Solar-Thermal Electric Power," in *Solar Energy for Earth, an AIAA Assessment,* pp. 32-45, American Institute of Aeronautics and Astronautics, New York, 1975.
2. L.L. Lukens, A.M. Perino, and S.G. Vandenender, *Preliminary Economic Analysis of Solar Irrigation Systems for Selected Locations,* Sand 77-1403, Sandia Laboratories, Albuquerque, New Mexico, 1977.
3. R.L. Alvis and L.L. Lukens, *Solar Irrigation Program Plan, Second Revision,* Sand 78-0308, Sandia Laboratories, Albuquerque, New Mexico, 1978.
4. "Solar Energy to Power Irrigation Pumps," *Agricultural Engineering,* July 1977, pp. 41-42.
5. G.H. Abernathy and T.R. Mancini, "Can Sunshine Power the Irrigation Pump?" *Agricultural Engineering,* October 1977, pp.39-40.
6. F.W. Lipps and H.F. Hildebrandt, "Central Receiver Systems for Irrigation Pumping and Cattle Feedmill Applications," *ibid.*
8. *Application of Solar Energy to the Supply of Industrial Process Hot Water,* Aerotherm Final Report, ERDA 77-235, p. 234, Energy Research and Development Administration, Washington, D.C., January 1977.
9. Jorgen Vindum and Keith Bentz, "Solar Energy for Industrial Process Hot Water," *Agricultural Engineering,* July 1977, pp. 37-40.
10. J.F. Lowry and R.S. Combes, "Study of Energy Use and Energy Conservation Modifications in the Georgia Poultry Industry," *Proceedings Symposium on Use of Solar Energy for Poultry and Livestock Production,* Auburn University, Auburn, Alabama, November, 1976.
11. T.C. Surbrook, J.S. Boyd, and H.C. Zindel, *Drying Animal Waste,* Research Report No. 117 Farm Science, pp 16-20, MSU-AES, Michigan State University, East Lansing, 1970.
12. J. DeBaerdemaeker and B.C. Horsfield, "Drying Animal Waste with Solar Energy," *loc cit* in reference 10.
13. W.H. Brown and R.E. Forbes, "Poultry House Heating and Manure Drying Utilizing Solar Energy," *ibid.*

V. ECONOMIC IMPLICATIONS

Intensive efforts to improve food production and marketing have focused largely on the development of labor-saving techniques and machinery. This reflects the fact that the food industry, which had grown rapidly and already reached a high level of technical efficiency, had done so at a time of relatively cheap and abundant energy. Decreasing supplies and rapidly increasing prices of fossil fuels now force a diversion of effort toward the search for alternate energy sources so that progress can continue.

Although commercial agriculture uses only a small fraction of all the energy consumed in the United States, that small fraction is crucial for efficient food and fiber production. Consequently, academic, industry, and government evaluations of the practicality of other energy sources are under way. Factors that must be studied include not only the obvious consideration of relative cost, but also availability, dependability, adaptability, and the effect of possible government incentives.

Evaluation of the economic feasibility of replacing fossil fuels with solar energy for heating is especially difficult because the daily availability of solar radiation (quantity and intensity) is unpredictable. However, the abundance, renewability, and cleanliness of solar energy are attractive and have stimulated many test projects, particularly in agriculture.

One such project[1] involved the development of methods for estimating the technical and economic feasibility of using solar energy to heat broiler houses and other farm buildings in Maryland. Because solar heating requires a relatively large initial investment but low operating costs, the Sum-of-Discounted-Costs method of analysis is applicable. This method permits a calculation of the operating time that must elapse before the overall cost of solar heating becomes lower than that of a conventional energy source. With little modification, the method can also determine the maximum initial investment that still allows a solar system to become less costly than a conventional fuel system in a specified number of years. The program for assessing cost-effectiveness is flexible so that it allows the insertion of changes in economic variables as they occur.

In the application of this method to heating Maryland broiler houses, solar energy was compared with propane on the basis of the following assumptions:

- 20-year operating period
- 20-year equipment lifetime
- Constant heating efficiency

127

- 5 flocks produced annually
- Similar pattern of house utilization each year
- Similar birds produced (similar sensible heat loss)
- Similar annual weather pattern
- Constant annual increase in fuel cost
- Heating systems exempt from property taxes, including increased value due to solar heating equipment
- Constant discount rate
- Cost data based on first quality collectors
- $21.53/m² ($2/ft²) collector cost — (Collectors in limited production now cost 10 to 20 times this much, but mass production or new technology could reduce cost by an unknown amount)

Table V-1 shows the results of the analysis, and Table V-2 shows the effects of system variables on and their relative importance to the feasibility of solar heating. Annual fuel price increases had the greatest effect, followed by the cost of solar collectors. The most economical solar heating system had small collectors and storage and an assumed 7% discount rate and 15% fuel-price inflation rate. Other assumed values for these variables increased the estimated solar heating costs.

Table V-1. Projected brooding and heating costs per 100 broilers for various energy sources

Cost interval, yr	Propane	Natural gas	Fuel oil	Electricity	Solar
1	$3.79	$2.71	$3.60	$4.66	$21.01
5	3.64	1.93	3.34	4.89	6.59
10	4.30	2.14	3.91	5.84	5.06
15	5.21	2.54	4.73	7.13	4.90
20	6.43	3.09	5.83	8.81	5.23

To calculate the fuel cost per 100 lb of ready-to-cook meat, divide the above figures by 2.92.

The study showed that solar heating of broiler houses in Maryland can become economically competitive with propane heating if the planned operating period can be made long enough for solar advantages (low operating costs) and propane disadvantages (rising price) to prevail over other factors. However, this raises the question of who will provide the longer-term financing. On the other hand, a more rapid rise in cost or interruption of the supply of conventional fuel would change the circumstances in favor of solar heating and shorten the time to economic feasibility. Meanwhile, the authors of the report suggest relaxation of federal, state, and local tax laws as one incentive to induce growers to turn to solar heating.

Table V-2. Projected solar vs propane 20-year broiler-house heating costs for various solar system sizes and economic conditions, assuming annual repairs costing 5% of purchase price, insurance costing 1% of equipment value, and 20-year averaged costs discounted to present value on a flock-by-flock basis

System	Collector area m²	Collector cost $/m²	Storage capacity 1000 liters	Solar portion of total heat %	Discount rate %	Annual fuel price increase %	Solar vs propane cost %	Solar breakeven period yr
1	185	21.53	22.7	41	7	15	−18.72	13–14
2	185	21.53	34.0	45	7	15	−17.48	14–15
3	37	21.53	45.4	63	7	15	−17.21	16–17
4	185	43.06	22.7	41	7	15	−8.66	17–18
5	185	43.06	34.0	45	7	15	−7.41	17–18
6	37	43.06	45.4	63	7	15	2.98	
7	185	86.11	22.7	41	7	15	11.47	Solar
8	185	86.11	34.0	45	7	15	12.72	costs
9	37	86.11	45.4	63	7	15	43.24	more
10	185	21.53	22.7	41	7	10	19.47	than
11	185	21.53	34.0	45	7	10	29.58	propane
12	37	21.53	45.4	63	7	10	59.15	
13	185	21.53	22.7	41	10	15	−11.65	15–16
14	185	21.53	34.0	45	10	15	−8.74	16–17
15	37	21.53	45.4	63	10	15	−3.14	19–20

Dickinson and Freeman[2] have studied the effect of such government incentives on the adoption of solar-assisted heat systems. They concluded in 1977 that the costs of industrial solar-thermal systems for processing heat were prohibitive so that growth of a mass market for such systems in the near future could not be expected without some sort of incentive such as tax rebates or low-interest, government-backed loans. Using life-cycle costing techniques, they showed that the allowed installed cost of a solar system in southwestern United States to provide process heat at a 10% real rate of return on the system investment was, under existing tax laws, only about $50–60/m² ($4.60–5.60/ft²). With a tax rebate on fossil-fuel saved combined with a 6% government-backed loan for 75% of the investment, the allowed solar-system cost would increase to about $180/m² ($17/ft²), allowing a more economically attractive investment in solar heating.

White[3] found that poultry brooding with solar heat was not feasible, given the present state of technology and the relationship between solar collector and installation costs on the one hand and the supplies and prices of alternative energy sources on the other. However, a broiler grower can save significant quantities of fuel and reduce costs by changing from whole-house to partial-house brooding.

Instead of distributing brooders throughout the whole house, the grower divides the house with a removable partition and equips only one section for brooding chicks. Estimated savings were 45% in fuel and 9% in costs (Tables V-3 and V-4). Addition of a hot-water supply heated by solar radiation and/or an auxiliary electric unit halves the consumption of fossil fuel (Table V-5). However, the solar and/or electric heat increases costs by almost 7% so that partial brooding with the added heating system costs only about 3% less than whole-house brooding with fossil-fuel heating.

Early tests in a research brooding facility equipped with solar-heated water[4] show that energy costs vary among brooding systems and that operating costs depend on the type of energy source (e.g., electricity, LPG, or solar radiation), the brooding

Table V-3. Estimated Alabama broiler-house costs with conventional heat and whole-house brooding

House: Metal, 11 x 102 m (36 x 336 ft) = 1122 m² (12,096 ft²)
Clear-span construction
Insulated roof and ends, side curtains
Eight 24-inch fans
Automatic feeders and waterers
No partition, chicks move freely, brooders distributed throughout house

Placement: 15,000 chicks/batch @ 5 batches/yr = 75,000 birds/yr

Brooding: 1 LPG brooder per 750 chicks
Fuel use — 155 liters (41 gal) per 1000 chicks
Fuel cost — 9.5¢/liter (36¢/gal)

Amortization: Building — 20 yr
Equipment — 7½ yr

INVESTMENT

Building @ $14/m² ($1.30/ft²)			$15,725
Equipment: Heating	$2980		
Feeding and watering	7920		10,900
		TOTAL	$26,625

CASH EXPENSES (excluding land and labor)

Insurance	$ 346		
Taxes	242		
Electricity	266		
Fuel	1107		
Repair and Maintenance	200		
Miscellaneous	250		$2411
Annual payment on investment			3570
		TOTAL	$5981

ANNUAL COST PER 1000 BIRDS $79.75

Table V-4. Estimated Alabama broiler-house costs with conventional heat and partial-house brooding

> **House:** Metal, 11 x 102 m (36 x 336 ft) = 1122 m² (12,096 ft²)
> Clear-span construction
> Insulated roof and ends, side curtains
> Eight 24-inch fans
> Automatic feeders and waterers
> Removable partition, brooding only in one section of house
>
> **Placement:** 15,000 chicks/batch @ 5 batches/yr = 75,000 birds/yr
>
> **Brooding:** 1 LPG brooder per 1500 chicks
> Fuel use — 85 liters (22.5 gal) per 1000 chicks
> Fuel cost — 9.5¢/liter (36¢/gal)
>
> **Amortization:** Building — 20 yr
> Equipment — 7½ yr

INVESTMENT

Building @ $14/m² ($1.30/ft²)			$15,725
Equipment: Heating	$2380		
Feeding and watering	8000		
			10,380
		TOTAL	$26,105

CASH EXPENSES (excluding land and labor)

Insurance	$332		
Taxes	242		
Electricity	266		
Fuel	606		
Repair and Maintenance	200		
Miscellaneous	300		
			$1946
Annual payment on investment			3505
		TOTAL	$5451

ANNUAL COST PER 1000 BIRDS $72.68

system design, and heating system management. Solar heating with an auxiliary electric unit may be more costly than heating with LPG alone. As might be expected, operating costs are generally lower the lower the required water temperature.

The water temperature required by the brooding system establishes the minimum acceptable storage temperature. Storage capacity is directly proportional to the difference between this minimum and the maximum storage temperature (about 95°C, or 203°F, for unpressurized storage). If the minimum acceptable storage temperature increases, the heat capacity of a given storage volume decreases. Reduced storage capacity requires an increase in auxiliary heating and, consequently, in operating cost. A higher minimum water temperature also reduces collector efficiency which is greater when colder water flows from storage to the collector.

Table V-5. Estimated Alabama broiler-house costs with solar heating and partial-house brooding

House: Metal, 11 x 102 m (36 x 336 ft) = 1122 m² (12,096 ft²)
            Clear-span construction
            Insulated roof and ends, side curtains
            Eight 24-inch fans
            Automatic feeders and waterers

Placement: 15,000 chicks/batch @ 5 batches/yr = 75,000 birds/yr

Brooding: 71.2-m² (776-ft²) solar collector area (0.19 Ac/Ah ratio, where Ac = collector area, Ah = house area
            11,355-liter (3000-gal) storage capacity
            Fuel use for auxiliary hot water — 2880 liter (761 gal) LPG
            Fuel cost — 9.5¢/liter (36¢/gal)

Amortization: Building — 20 yr
                        Solar unit — 15 yr
                        Equipment — 7½ yr

INVESTMENT

Building @ $14/m² ($1.30/ft²)			$15,725
Equipment: Collector	$6129		
Storage (3 tanks)	1500		
Pumps, pipes, valves, etc.	3224		
Auxiliary hot water	680		
Feeding and watering	7920		
			19,453
		TOTAL	$35,178

CASH EXPENSES (excluding land and labor)

Insurance	$457		
Taxes	242		
Electricity	392		
Fuel	300		
Repair and Maintenance	274		
Miscellaneous	300		
			$1965
Annual payment on investment			3851
		TOTAL	$5816
ANNUAL COST PER 1000 BIRDS			$77.55

Energy used to pump water through the system can also significantly affect operating cost. Pumps of the wrong size and management that operates pumps excessively can consume almost as much energy as heating.

High capital costs and long-term amortization of initial investment are major deterrents to installation of solar heating systems. As long as collector and storage costs increase faster than the inflation rate, and interest rates remain above 10%, elaborate solar heating systems will be difficult to justify economically. Nevertheless, the feasibility of solar-heating should be judged for the individual circumstances of each case, based on an estimate of comparative unit energy costs for solar and conventional heating, including the following steps:

1. Calculate energy requirements.
2. Calculate component sizes for systems capable of supplying an acceptable portion of total energy requirements. Assess all suitable and technically feasible solar systems. Exclusive use of solar radiation for all energy needs will usually require a grossly oversized system. Investigate systems of various capacities that can supply different acceptable fractions of the total energy requirement.
3. Estimate capital costs for each system.
4. Estimate yearly operating and maintenance costs.
5. Amortize capital investment over the useful life of the system.
6. Total costs over operating life and calculate average annual ownership cost.
7. Divide annual cost by expected useful annual energy yield to determine unit energy cost.
8. Compare unit costs for solar and other systems, taking into account the lengths of time over which the costs were averaged.

ECONOMIC IMPLICATIONS

References

1. Jarvis L. Cain and Donald L. Van Dyne, *Economic Feasibility of Heating Maryland Broiler Houses with Solar Energy,* MP 898, University of Maryland Agricultural Experiment Station, College Park, February 1977.
2. W.C. Dickinson and J.H. Freeman, *An Economic Methodology for Solar Assisted Industrial Process Heat Systems: The Effect of Government Incentives,* UCRL-52254, Lawrence Livermore Laboratories, University of California, Livermore, June 1977.
3. Morris White, "An Economic Appraisal of Use of Solar Energy in Broiler Production," *Proceedings Symposium on Use of Solar Energy for Poultry and Livestock Production,* Auburn University, Auburn, Alabama, November 1976.
4. Donald H. Van Dyne and Jarvis L. Cain, "A Method of Estimating Technical and Economic Feasibility of Solar Heating Systems for Broiler Houses and Other Farm Buildings," *Agricultural and Resource Economics Information Series A-10,* University of Maryland, College Park, 1977.

VI. CONCLUSIONS

This monograph examines the practical and economic feasibility of using solar radiation as an alternative to fossil fuels for a source of thermal energy in agriculture. Potential user groups are farmers and agribusinessmen involved in production and processing of agricultural commodities. Since these users must compete world-wide in the production of food and fiber, cost and return of any energy system are of primary concern. Although thermal energy accounts for a relatively minor part of total production costs in most agricultural applications, it is often an essential factor for achieving maximum production and maintaining high quality.

Much of the thermal energy for agriculture is needed at relatively low temperatures (below 250°F) readily attained with solar energy systems. The discussion in Chapter II of the effect of climatic variables on the capture, storage, and use of solar energy indicates the paradox in the United States: solar energy is most available in areas where the need is relatively small. For example, natural sunshine and wind are generally adequate to dry some grains without engineered solar systems in the southeastern states where the abundant sunshine is also advantageous for solar collection.

Nevertheless, the country as a whole does have ample daily insolation (2000-2800 Btu/ft²) during the early harvest season so that solar energy could be collected to speed drying and curing as insurance against loss of quality. Also, the agricultural requirements of large amounts of heat for production buildings such as poultry houses are concentrated in the relatively sunny southeast and west coast areas. These areas are excellent targets for exploitation of solar energy because the mean insolation during cold periods is as high as 900–1100 Btu/ft².

Solar technology (Chapter III) continues to advance. Presently available low-temperature lower-cost systems, such as flat-plate or evacuated-tube collectors with liquid or rock-bed storage, are readily adapted to agricultural use and work well in such applications as crop and grain drying and space and water heating. Liquid or air heat transfer fluids are compatible with most commercial heating and drying systems used in agriculture. The use of high-temperature collectors such as central receivers and other focusing devices that track the sun will probably be severely limited by their specialized character and high initial cost.

The most economically promising agricultural applications of solar energy (Chapter IV) include the heating of livestock shelters and greenhouses and the drying of crops and grain. Basic plant breeding of some cereal grains may alter their genetic makeup to better adapt them to intermittent drying fueled mainly by solar energy systems. Also promising, but at a somewhat higher cost, are certain energy-intensive applications such as the manufacture of feed, agricultural chemicals, and fertilizer and the irrigation of otherwise unproductive land.

Another characteristic of agricultural production that makes it an attractive prospect for solar exploitation is the frequent location of production facilities on relatively inexpensive, non-rural land in isolated areas far from natural gas lines. Such isolated farms and other agricultural enterprises are at a disadvantage in obtaining fuel, making them more receptive to a renewable energy source such as solar radiation.

Economic considerations (Chapter V) show that the application of solar energy systems requires careful assessment and projection into the future of many variables. For example, rapidly changing agricultural technology tends to make farm machinery, buildings, and production facilities obsolete in a relatively few years so that solar system installations must be amortized over a fairly short time span of 15-20 years. Multiple use, such as combined greenhouse and residence heating, livestock-shelter and grain drying, and partial-house poultry brooding, helps to brighten the outlook for solar-system application and shorten the pay-back period. Special incentives such as tax relief are also beneficial.

Readers can find more details on the agricultural use of solar energy in the cited references and from such agencies as the National Climatic Center and the U.S. Department of Energy.

Glossary

Absorber The part of a solar collector that receives solar radiation and transforms it into heat. Usually a solid surface, it passes energy on to the transfer fluid. The transfer fluid, in the form of a black liquid, can itself sometimes be the absorber.

Absorptivity The fraction of incident radiant energy that is absorbed, that is, neither reflected nor transmitted by the absorbing surface.

Active system (solar) A collector-thermal storage-transfer fluid assembly which converts radiation into useful heat and circulates the heat with the aid of energy from a non-solar source.

Agricultural and industrial process heat Both an end use for thermal energy and the name applied to that part of the national solar program devoted to developing solar technology for this end use.

Air exchange The rate of replacement of air volume, expressed as number of changes per house per unit time. One air change/hour means that all air in the house will be replaced by the end of one hour.

Animal waste A mixture of wet and dry animal excrement varying in moisture content from under 20% to over 90%, depending on method of management.

Aquaculture Cultivation of water plant and animal life.

ASHRAE Acronym for the American Society of Heating, Refrigeration and Air Conditioning Engineers, located at 345 E.47 St., New York, NY 10017. ASHRAE Handbooks are sources of basic data on heating and air conditioning.

Atmospheric turbidity Haze.

Auxiliary energy Energy from a non-solar source used to supplement the output of a solar energy system. It supplies the full load during periods when the solar system is inoperable.

Bioconversion Conversion of organic matter by biological processes to more useful forms of stored energy, for example, the digestion of solid wastes by microorganisms to form methane.

Biomass Material derived from growing organisms, for example, agricultural products and residues, trees, wood and bark residues, animal manures, and algae.

Black body An ideal body which absorbs all radiation incident on its surface. It also emits the maximum possible radiation at any given body temperature. Its absorptivity and emissivity equal 1 and its reflectivity is 0.

Brooder A heat-delivery system used to warm livestock, primarily during early life.

Btu   British thermal unit, the amount of heat required to raise the temperature of one pound of water one degree Fahrenheit, equal to 1054 joules.

Bulk curing   Drying and thermal treatment of bulk quantities of agricultural products such as tobacco.

Capital intensive   Requiring a relatively large initial investment as compared with operating and labor costs.

Climate   Prevailing regional meteorological conditions including temperature, precipitation, solar radiation, humidity, and wind. Should not be confused with weather.

Collector,

    air   A solar collector in which the transfer fluid is air.

    concentrating or focusing   A collector system that intensifies solar radiation by focusing to achieve higher temperatures.

    evacuated-tube   A form of flat-plate collector made of concentric tubes in which the inner tubes comprise the absorbing surfaces and transfer-fluid channels, and a vacuum between the inner tubes and the transparent outer walls reduces heat losses.

    flat-plate   A collector with a flat absorbing surface that does not concentrate (intensify) the received radiation.

    high-temperature   A collector in which the operating temperature of the transfer fluid is at least 115°C (240°F).

    liquid   A collector in which the transfer fluid is a liquid.

    low-temperature   A collector in which the operating temperature of the transfer fluid is less than 115°C (240°F).

    parabolic trough   A concentrating collector in which the walls of a trough with a parabolic cross section reflect radiation to a focal axis.

Collector efficiency   Ratio of the energy collected to the total radiant energy incident on a solar collector.

Collector tilt angle   Angle by which a collector surface is slanted upward from the horizontal.

Concentration ratio or *factor*   Ratio between the radiation intensity at the focus of a concentrating solar collector and the intensity of the solar radiation incident on the collector site. Ratios have exceeded 10,000 for some collectors.

Condensate   Liquid condensed from its vapor.

Corrosion inhibitor   Chemical added to transfer fluid to reduce corrosion of metals in system.

Deep stacking manure   A method for stabilizing manure involving elevated temperature and microbial activity.

Deep well   A well that taps subsurface water, usually over 100 ft deep.

Delivery system   The part of a heating and domestic hot water system through which the transfer fluid distributes heat.

Desiccant   A material that readily takes up and retains water, useful as a drying agent.

Design life   The period during which a heating and domestic hot water system is expected to perform without requiring major repair or replacement.

Differential thermostat   A thermal control that depends on the difference between two temperatures rather than on either temperature alone.

Diffuse radiation   Solar radiation scattered by atmospheric gas, dust, and vapor so that it arrives at the collector from all directions rather than directly from the sun.

Direct conversion   Conversion of sunlight directly into electricity without intermediate processes.

Direct radiation   Solar radiation arriving at the collector directly from the sun without atmospheric scattering.

Discount Rate   Rate at which an anticipated higher future value is reduced to the present value in calculations of projected costs.

Drain-down collector system   A collector system in which the transfer liquid drains from the collector and associated plumbing into storage when the system is idle.

Emissivity   The ratio of the energy radiated by a body in unit time per unit area to that radiated by a black body at the same temperature.

Energy   The capacity to do work. It has different forms, such as thermal, mechanical, electrical, and chemical, which can be transformed into each other, and is expressed in different units, such as Btu and kilowatt-hours. The international standard unit (SI) is the joule, equal to a watt-second.

Eutectic salts   Chemical substances, such as Glauber's salt, with convenient melting points that make them useful for heat storage. Melting absorbs relatively large amounts of heat (latent heat of fusion) without a temperature change. The heat is released when the salts freeze.

Farrowing   Giving birth by swine.

Farrowing cycle   Time for farrowing scheduled in swine production.

Foot-candle   Unit of illuminance equal to 1 lumen/ft^2, the illuminance produced 1 ft away from a light source of 1 candle. A bright sun directly overhead produces an illuminance of the order of 10,000 foot-candles on the earth's surface.

Fossil fuel   A fuel, such as coal, oil, and natural gas, formed from the remains of plant or animal life from an earlier geological period.

Geothermal energy   Energy drawn from the earth's internal heat as at hot springs.

Glauber's salt   Sodium decahydrate ($Na_2SO_4 \cdot 10H_2O$), useful for heat storage because it melts at 32°C (90°F), absorbing about 104 Btu/lb in latent heat of fusion.

Glazing   A transparent or translucent barrier (glass or plastic), such as a window, skylight, greenhouse roof, or solar collector cover, which admits light but restricts heat loss by reradiation and convection.

Global radiation   The total radiation incident on the collector expressed in watt/m^2. It is the sum of diffuse and direct radiation.

Greenhouse blanket   Removable material designed to reduce heat exchange between the greenhouse and its surroundings.

Greenhouse effect   Heating of an enclosure due to the selective transmission properties of its transparent or translucent cover which readily transmits shortwave solar radiation to the interior but blocks longwave reverse radiation.

Heat exchanger   A device that transfers heat from one fluid to another without direct contact or intermixing.

Heat-transfer medium   A liquid, gas, or solid used to transport thermal energy.

Humidity (relative)   The ratio of the existing moisture content of the air to the saturation moisture content at the same temperature.

Illumination   The visible radiant energy incident per unit time per unit area at a point on an intercepting surface.

Infiltration   The uncontrolled air leakage into a building through cracks and interstices or around doors and windows due to wind impact or pressure differences between inside and outside.

Insensible heat   Heat that does not contribute to a temperature rise, as, for example, latent heat of fusion or of evaporation. See *Sensible heat, Latent heat.*

Insolation   Intensity of solar radiation at a point on a horizontal plane on the earth's surface, measured in such units as watts/m^2 or Btu/hr-ft^2. *Direct insolation* is intensity of rays arriving unscattered from the sun's direction. *Diffuse insolation* is intensity of rays arriving from all directions except that of the sun after scattering by the atmosphere. *Global insolation* is the sum of the direct and diffuse components.

Insulation (thermal)   Barrier to heat loss or gain by conduction or convection, usually containing large numbers of small dead-air spaces.

Intensive agriculture   Method for increasing agricultural productivity by investing more capital and labor without expanding acreage.

Irradiance   Total radiant energy incident per unit time per unit area at a point on an intercepting surface.

Irrigation pond   Surface storage of water for irrigation.

joule   Unit of energy, equal to the work done (energy expended) when the point of application of a force of 1 newton moves through a distance of 1 meter. It also equals the heat produced when a 1-ampere electric current flows for 1 second through a 1-ohm resistance (potential difference of 1 volt).

kPa   Kilopascal, equal to 1000 pascal. Pascal is the international pressure unit equivalent to 1 newton/m^2. One kilopascal equals 0.145 psi or 7.5 mm Hg.

kw   Kilowatt, equal to 1000 watts. One watt is the unit of power equivalent to a 1-ampere electric current flowing between two points with a potential difference of 1 volt.

kwhr   Kilowatt-hour, unit of energy equal to the work done in 1 hour by a power of 1 kilowatt. Also equal to 3,600,000 joules.

langley   Old unit of solar radiation energy density, equivalent to 1 gram-calorie/cm², usually used to express radiation intensity in langley/min. One langley/min equals 221.2 Btu/hr-ft².

Latent heat Change in the heat content of a substance without a change in temperature, usually accompanied by a change in state such as melting (latent heat of fusion) or evaporation (latent heat of evaporation).

Life cycle cost Estimate of total cost including the initial expense of purchase and installation and operating expense over expected lifespan. Usually includes discounting of future costs to reflect changes in the relative value of money with time.

LPG Liquid petroleum gas such as propane and butane, compressed for convenient storage and used as fuel or as new raw material for chemical synthesis.

Livestock shelter Building used primarily to house livestock or poultry.

Micron, μ (or micrometer, μm) Millionth of a meter, commonly used to express the wavelength of light: ultraviolet — less than 0.4μ, visible — 0.4–0.7μ, and infrared — longer than 0.7μ.

Moisture content Amount of moisture expressed as a percentage of either the total, or wet, weight (wet weight basis, w.b.) or the weight of the dry portion (dry weight basis, d.b.).

OTEC Ocean thermal energy conversion, the use of the temperature difference between warm upper and cold deeper levels of the ocean to drive a low-pressure turbine for direct motive power or generation of electricity.

Passive system A solar energy system in which collected heat circulates naturally without the aid of devices powered by non-solar sources.

Payback A traditional measure of the economic viability of an investment project, defined in several ways. For a solar energy system, payback can be defined in terms of the number of years required to accumulate fuel savings equal to the initial capital cost. Payback may not accurately represent the total life-cycle value.

Phase change With regard to substances, the change from one physical state (solid, liquid, or gas) to another. See *Latent heat*.

Photosynthesis Conversion of light to chemical energy by chlorophyll-containing cells in green plants with the synthesis of organic substances from inorganic components.

Photovoltaic effect Direct conversion of light into electricity in solid-state devices.

Prep stall Dairy area where cows are washed and prepared for milking.

Pyranometer An instrument for measuring total insolation from all directions (global radiation) including both direct and diffuse components. Also called *Global pyranometer, Solarimeter.*

Pyrheliometer An instrument for measuring direct insolation only.

Radiation Propagation of energy by electromagnetic waves. Also used for the energy and the waves themselves.

Rankine engine   A heat engine for which the Rankine thermodynamic cycle represents an ideal standard. It includes a condensable fluid which is pumped under pressure to a boiler where heat is added; an expander (turbine) in which the hot fluid does work; and a condenser which transfers heat from the fluid to the atmosphere before the next compression. One example is a steam engine.

Receiver, central   The structure at the focal region of an array of solar collectors where sunlight is concentrated and high temperature heat is removed for special purposes.

Reflectivity   The fraction of incident radiant energy that is reflected, that is, neither transmitted nor absorbed by the reflecting surface. Reflectivity + transmissivity + absorptivity = 1.

Reradiation   Emission of radiant energy after previous absorption. Wavelengths depend on the temperature of the emitting body. Reradiated wavelengths are longer than those absorbed when the reradiating body (e.g., a greenhouse interior) is cooler than the source (the sun) of the previously absorbed rays. See *Greenhouse effect.*

Retrofit   For solar energy systems, to adapt collectors to existing buildings. More generally, to add newly developed elements to an existing structure.

R factor   Unit of thermal resistance, equal to the reciprocal of thermal conductivity, used to compare the insulating values of different materials. The higher the R factor, the greater the insulation.

Saline pond   A pond containing a nonuniform salt concentration designed for combined solar collection and storage.

Sensible heat   Heat that contributes to a temperature rise (thus, heat that can be "felt"). See *Insensible heat, Latent heat.*

Solar

    altitude   Angle of the sun-earth line above the horizontal.

    azimuth   Angle between the north-south line and the projection of the sun-earth line on a horizontal plane at the collector site.

    constant   Intensity of solar radiation on a surface perpendicular to the sun's rays above the earth's atmosphere (at the sun-earth distance but free of atmospheric absorption and scattering), equal to 1.353 watts/m^2, 1.940 cal/min-cm^2, or 429.2 Btu/hr-ft^2 ($\pm1.6\%$).

    declination   Angle between the sun-earth line and a plane through the earth's equator.

    energy   Energy generated in the sun at temperatures of many millions of degrees. The energy radiated into space is the composite result of emission and absorption characteristics of the sun's outer layers. For earth applications, primary interest is in wavelengths between 0.3 and 3.0 microns.

    thermal conversion (STC)   Conversion of collected solar radiation into heat and then electricity.

    time   Hours of the day reckoned by the apparent position of the sun. Noon is the time of maximum solar altitude. Solar time rarely agrees exactly with local standard time.

window An imaginary frame through which the sun's rays must pass to reach the solar collector.

Storage,

desiccant-regeneration Storage by use of heat to remove moisture from a desiccant material (regeneration), preparing it for use in a future drying operation.

phase-change Heat storage by melting or evaporating a suitable material. Heat is recovered when the material freezes or condenses. Since temperature need not change, the stored heat is called "insensible."

liquid Heat storage by means of a temperature increase in a liquid ("sensible" heat). Capacity depends on the liquid's specific heat and temperature rise.

rock-bed Heat storage by means of a temperature increase in a rock or pebble bed (or other solid material). Capacity depends on a large temperature difference between the storage bed and the circulating heat-transfer fluid.

thermal A means for holding heat for future use.

Stratification (thermal) Vertical temperature distribution in liquid storage with cooler (denser) water at the bottom and hotter water at the top.

Temperature,

ambient Air temperature around the solar installation.

dewpoint Air temperature at which dew starts to form (water vapor condenses).

dry bulb Air temperature read on a standard thermometer.

wet bulb Reduced temperature read on a thermometer with its bulb wrapped in wet material from which water is evaporating. The difference between dry and wet bulb temperatures is used to determine relative humidity.

Therm 100,000 Btu, used to express the heat content of natural gas.

Transfer fluid Gas or liquid used to carry accumulated heat away from the collector. May also be used for storage and delivery of heat to point of use.

Transmissivity The fraction of incident radiant energy that is transmitted, that is, neither reflected nor absorbed. Transmissivity of a solar collector cover varies with the glazing thickness, composition, and cleanliness, and with the angle of incidence of solar radiation.